Farm and Smallholder Fencing

by

Michael Roberts

Edited by Sara Roadnight

Photographs by Michael Roberts

ISBN: 0947870 423

© Gold Cockerel Books

Published by Gold Cockerel Books
2004

Contents

Acknowledgements

I would like to thank Gallagher Power Fence (UK) Ltd for all their kind assistance and for the use of their photographic material, Gripple Ltd for being so helpful, and Sidney and Mark Dallyn, fencing suppliers and contractors from Parracombe, North Devon, for their valuable time, experience and knowledge of fencing and fencing materials.

I must stress that all fencers have their own ways of working, and while I believe I have covered most methods, there will always be variations and different ways of approaching problems. I respect these differences as they have been well tried and tested while being handed down with modifications over the generations. I am certainly not claiming that any method is the 'correct' one, as each job is unique and affected by so many different factors.

Farm and Smallholder Fencing

Reasons for fencing:

1) To prevent livestock getting out.
2) To separate your neighbour's stock from your own.
3) To control animal diseases (worms, foot rot etc.)
4) To segregate different types of stock.
5) To foster good neighbourly relations.
6) To rest, spray or fertilize fields.
7) Good fencing increases the value of your holding.
8) Good fencing makes your farm or smallholding look tidy.

Reasons why livestock get out:

1) They are short of food or water.
2) They want to mate.
3) They want to fight.
4) They are frightened of fire, floodwater, predators, low-flying aircraft, hot air balloons, etc.
5) Bloody mindedness.
6) Someone has left the gate open.

Chapter 1   Tools

We start with a few notes on the tools required for fencing. You will need most if not all these items if you have a lot of fencing to do.

Claw hammer

One tip here for when you are using your hammer in wet conditions: if the hammer slips while you are fixing staples or large nails, dry the hitting surface on your trousers and you will find the hammer stops slipping.

Fencing pliers

These are essential tools for fencers. They are multi-purpose and can cut wire, strain wire, twist wire and remove staples. There are several qualities on the market but it is best to buy the most expensive as the cheaper ones wear out quickly or break.

Hacksaw

These are very useful for large nails that bend while being knocked in. They are sometimes very difficult to get out, and to save time and make the job look neat, just hacksaw them off.

1.5" Wood chisel

Try to buy one with a composite handle. These are useful for mortising and/ or notching straining posts.

Hand saw

I use a small metal bow saw as the teeth are wide set and it cuts easily through green timber without binding or getting stuck. It's always worth having a few new blades handy.

Hacksaw, handsaw, chisel, brace and bit, tape measure, pencil, fencing pliers, claw hammer and baler twine.

Builder's spirit level

Use a long one for checking uprightness of gates or straining posts etc, and the level of gates. I also use a small one when boring holes into gate posts to ensure they are level.

Pencil and tape measure

Make sure that your tape measure is the large metal variety so that you can span wide gateways etc. with it.

Baler twine

This is essential when you are working out fencing lines. Notch an oblong of ply board at both ends and wind your baler twine onto it for storage.

Brace and Bits

I prefer a hand brace as I often seem to find electric drills "die" at the critical moment. Maybe I'm biased! You will need several sizes of bit: an auger bit (size 22mm) for boring holes for gate irons, a wood bit (size 8mm) for boring holes on gate hinges, and a wood bit (size 6mm) for boring holes for nails through thin stakes to stop them splitting.

A pair of loppers

These are handy for cutting back branches and brambles from a working area, or for the odd root in a post hole. Try to get anvil head loppers as these last longer than the criss-cross type.

Sledge hammer

I use one of these for driving in stops for leaners against straining posts. I don't use a sledge hammer to drive in stakes as it has a habit of splitting them open at the top thus weakening them and reducing their life span.

Loppers, rings and ring pliers, wire cutters, gloves, bar strainers, builders' spirit level, Monkey strainer and wire bender.

A mawl

This a kind of sledge hammer with either a broad metal, or a wooden or hard rubber head. Some people swear by these for banging in stakes, but I have always used a Drival or thumper.

Drival or thumper

This also has names such as bodybuilder or mankiller and others which are unprintable! It certainly pushes posts in without splitting them and can be used by one or two people. It is hard work but ideal for small acreages, and certainly warms you up on frosty days!

Crowbar

This is normally round in section and is used to make a pilot hole for a stake to go in. It will detect any stones and if you move it round in a circle they can normally be pushed aside to allow the post a straight downward passage. In stony soil a crowbar is useful for removing stones or rocks when you are digging out a gate post hole for example.

Spade

It is usually a matter of personal preference whether one chooses a straight or curved spade. I use a rabbiting spade which I have had for years, but a straight spade does make cleaner cuts.

Rammer

These are normally home made affairs no wider than 3" (7.5 cm) to be able to get round posts in tight holes. I have seen them in agricultural merchants, welded to the tops of crow bars.

Small bolt croppers

These are essential as wire cutters, particularly for high tensile wire which is very tough to cut.

Livestock wire straining clamp. bill hook, measuring stick, rammer, ear muffs, spade, chain saw, crow bar, sledge hammer, Drival, tin.

Rings and ring pliers

There are several makes of these on the market. They are like wire pliers but with a magazine of metal clips attached. They are used for clipping wire netting to plain wire or joining two types of wire netting together.

Good gloves

These are very important, and anyone who thinks it is sissy to wear gloves, hasn't been fencing. Apart from handling barbed wire and unrolling livestock wire in which you can easily get your fingers trapped, the main problem is splinters from the treated stakes or timber. These splinters are just as poisonous as blackthorn. A good pair of gloves or gauntlets is best, particularly in winter as they keep the wrists warm (warm wrists, warm hands) and they do stop barbed wire from wrapping around your lower sleeves.

Bar strainer

This is a hand strainer for levering wire tight round posts and is good for tensioning short lengths of wire.

Monkey strainer

Without this you cannot tension any long lengths of wire unless you are using the Gripple system. Some people think that you can use a vehicle to pull wire taut but you do not have sufficient control or 'feel' doing it this way and could end up breaking the wire. Other people use electric winches which work well because there is quite a lot of control.

The Monkey strainer has two wire-gripping sets of jaws one of which can be used as an anchor, a six foot chain in between and a ratchet handle for straining. To tension either a single wire or a livestock wire, attach whichever you are using to the gripping jaws and anchor the other end of the strainer to a tractor or post, etc. Check that the ratchet chain is not twisted then draw the surplus chain through the ratchet head and start to pull in the chain with the ratchet handle. When you find that the handle is too hard to move it

14

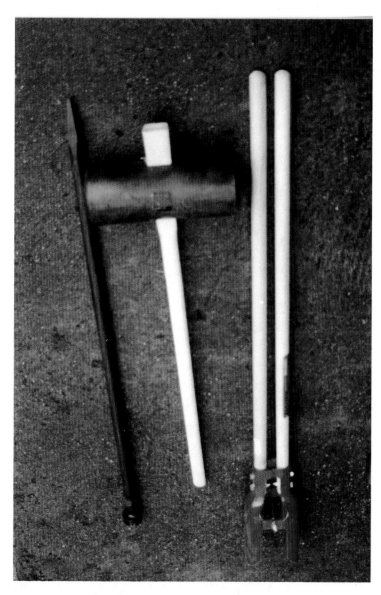

Crowbar/rammer, mawl and Shuv holer.

means that the wire should be taut. If you run out of ratchet chain you may find that you have to move the anchoring point further away or move the gripping jaws down the wire to achieve the correct tension. Once you have secured the wire firmly with staples you can release the Monkey strainer and take it away. When you get used to working with it you'll find it quite easy but, as with all tools there is a knack to it.

Livestock wire straining clamp

This is made from two lengths of 4" x 2" (10 x 5cm) wood, 42" (107cm) long which are bolted together vertically round the livestock wire, using three 6" x .5" (15 x 1.5cm) bolts. A chain is incorporated on the top and bottom bolts and is attached to the tensioning tool. Make sure that the wooden clamp is vertical and that the point of attachment to the tensioning tool is equidistant on the chain. You will need a spanner for this as well. It is possible to buy purpose made metal clamps.

Chain saw

This must be one of the most important items among a fencer's tools. Chain saws are much safer than they used to be but are still potentially very dangerous and there have been some horrific injuries caused by them. If you are not very familiar with them or have had no experience at all, you must go on a day course and learn how to handle them, not only for your own safety but also for the good of the machine. I once lent my chain saw to a so-called experienced user, and it came back a wreck. There are particular ways of cutting timber, keeping the chain sharp and handling and maintaining the machine that you would only learn from an experienced trainer. Included in your chain saw kit should be ear muffs (defenders), glasses or visor, hard hat, gloves, a stout pair of boots, a chain saw oil can, a can of mixed petrol, a spanner-cum-screwdriver for tensioning slack chains and a plastic blade cover. If you have a fair amount of work to do it is best to have several fresh blades and chains with you so you are not held up by having to sharpen your chain; this can always be done when you get home after dark.

Bar strainer

Wire dispenser or jenny

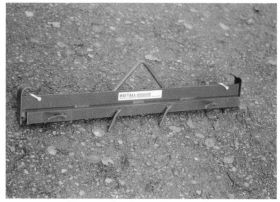

Livestock wire straining clamp

17

One tip if you are wearing Wellingtons (with toe protectors), don't tuck your trousers into your Wellingtons; if you do your boots will quickly fill up with wood chippings from the saw blade!

Double spade or Shuv holer for making post holes

Some people prefer these to a single spade. It is a matter of choice, and certainly there is less kneeling on the ground involved if you use one of these.

A tin or plastic cup

You will need one of these for emptying post holes. Very often, especially in wet conditions, the post hole fills up with water as you are digging it out.

A wire bender

This has all kinds of names. It is a short length of flat iron with an eighth of an inch hole through it to take the end of a piece of fencing wire and bend it back to tidy up the look of a fence.

A measuring stick

This is a length of wooden lath onto which you can mark wire heights to ensure that they are evenly spaced on each stake.

Kneeler

If you are digging out a post hole by hand it does sometimes get rather wet or stony under the knees. A chunk of thick foam rubber covered in a plastic feed bag and secured with duck (waterproof) tape does the trick making a useful kneeler.

Bill hook or slasher

Some people prefer to use these instead of loppers. It is entirely a matter of choice.

Chapter 2   Materials

Materials for fencing can be roughly split into two categories, wood and metal.

Wood

Most fencing posts and rails are made of treated soft wood. These products are available from agricultural merchants or estate timber yards.

Heartwood cleft oak and sweet chestnut are very durable and will last in the ground as long as treated timber and longer off the ground as rails. Cleft ash and willow are also suitable off the ground as rails, and willow can be used as stops for leaners or as short stakes at ground level to help strengthen posts (see chapter 6).

The soft wood is pine and fir and a large proportion is imported these days from the Baltic States although some is grown in the British Isles. It is sawn into lengths, debarked and then made into round or square posts and rails and pointed stakes. The finished timber is then stacked onto trolleys and rolled into a huge metal tube or vacuum chamber where it will receive its preserving treatment. The door is firmly closed and the air and moisture are drawn out; then the vacuum is released and a preserving fluid containing chrome, copper and other chemicals is introduced and pressurised to force it into the timber. (Arsenic has now been dropped by most saw mills.) The chamber is then vacuumised again to draw off excess fluids and help dry the timber. There are several trade names for the preserving fluids used such as Cellcure, Protim or Tanilith from which comes the word tanalise. The treatment extends the life of the timber, particularly for outdoor applications, but in very dry summers it can make certain woods rather brittle which could cause the odd stake or rail to snap. The preserving process does alter the structure of the wood but this is a small price to pay for a fence that will last 20 to 30 years.

Rolls of livestock wire

Stakes and posts

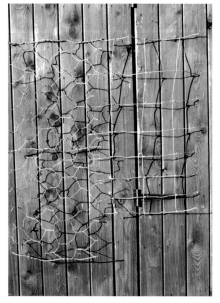

Sheep wire and pig wire.

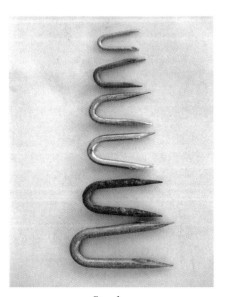

Staples

20

Metal

All the following metal products can be bought from agricultural merchants, estate timber yards, some builders' merchants or through specialist fencing equipment suppliers.

Gate furniture

The hinges on a gate are known as gate furniture and are made up of hooks and bands. There are several different ways of fixing the top hook; some are bolted through the post, some are fitted round it and some are secured with a plate and coach bolts. The bottom hook is normally hammered in or fixed with a plate and coach bolts. The bands, which are the pieces fixed to the gate, come in two sizes. The top band is always longer than the bottom one and both are bolted through the gate. You can get adjustable bottom hinge bands but these should be used with care as they can weaken the gate.

Gate fasteners

There are many kinds of fastener available, simple hooks, sliding bolts, latches, and clasps and eyes. Do remember that horses and cows sometimes have a habit of chewing and worrying some fasteners, with the result that the gate swings open, so it is as well to add a simple chain fastener as backup!

Wire

Plain wire is normally available in 3.15mm or 2.50mm thickness and is made of either mild or high tensile steel. It is sold in coils. Barbed wire is either heavy duty or light and is also available in mild or high tensile steel. High tensile barbed wire holds its tension better than that made of mild steel which does stretch and sag after a while. All barbed wire is sold on reels.

Livestock wire

This used to be called pig wire and the Americans call it woven wire. Old fashioned sheep wire is rarely seen now and was normally used with metal posts to make a temporary fence. Livestock wire is used these days for horses, cattle, sheep, deer, pigs and pheasants, and to keep out badgers. It is sold in 50m and 100m length rolls which are always labeled with information on the grade and spacing of the wires.

There are four different grades of livestock wire:

- HT: High tensile
- B: Heavy grade (mild steel)
- C: Medium grade (mild steel)
- L: Light grade (mild steel)

A label might read C8-80-15. C = medium grade, 8 = the number of horizontal wires, 80 = 80cms, the height of the roll, 15 = 15cm gaps between the verticals. This roll of wire will be suitable for sheep.

Another example might read HT13-190-22. HT = High tensile with 13 horizontal wires, 190 = 190cms, the height of the roll, 22 = 22cm gaps between the verticals. This roll of wire will be suitable for deer.

It's a good idea to get advice from your contractor or agricultural merchant on the best type of wire for your needs.

Some plain, barbed and livestock wire is made with a green finish but tends to be more expensive.

Wire netting

This is for use with poultry, pheasants or waterfowl and comes in a choice of heights: 3ft, 4ft, 5ft and 6ft (90cms, 122cms, 152cms and 183cms). The mesh is available in .5", 1" and 2" sizes (1.5cms, 2.5cms and 5cms). There are several lengths available from 10m to 50m. Beware of cheap imports from the Far East as the galvanizing can be very poor.

Gamenet

This is made of plastic rather than metal and provides a cheap, light fencing material. The mesh size is 1" x .75" (2.5cms x 2cms) with heights of 5ft, 6ft and 7ft (152cms, 183cms and 213cms). The rolls are available in 100m lengths. Gamenet is best secured onto posts and stakes with wooden battens as a strong wind could easily tear the netting away from staples.

Radisseurs or wire strainers

These are wire strainers which are incorporated into the fence for tensioning plain, mild or high tensile wire. They have a ratchet system and you will need a spanner or special tool to tension the wire with them.

Eye bolts

These are also used for tensioning plain wire and are left in place on the fence. They do rust after a few years and only have a short tensioning length.

Staples

These come in several sizes. The normal size to use when fencing is 1.5"(4cms) or 2" (5cms) on straining posts. Smaller sized staples, 1" (2.5cms) or .75" (2cms) are used to secure wire netting. Barbed staples are superior to plain ones.

Nails

The nails most commonly used for fencing are 4", 5" and 6" ones; these are available in bright or galvanized steel; galvanized nails are best for outdoor use.

There are various other gadgets for fencing on the market such as crimp or joining sleeves which require a special crimping tool, but these are mainly used by contractors.

Chapter 3 Planning

Fencing comes in two types, brand new and renewed. Most people are faced with renewing existing fencing lines but in the case of a farm being split up, new fencing lines may have to be established. It is important to check your deeds or paperwork to make sure that what you have bought or rented tallies with what is down on paper. Normally there are existing fences, walls or marker posts, but if you are not sure check with the local land surveyor or your solicitor. Mistakes can be costly and there are unscrupulous people out there.

Whether you are putting in new lines of fencing or renewing old ones, you will need to plan your field(s). Try to make the lines as straight as possible to keep down the cost of materials and ensure easy access for farm machinery. Most fields are regular in shape but old ones frequently are not, particularly if there is a stream running along one side. If there is a narrow pointed area in a field, fence it off and the same with difficult corners or boggy patches. When the farmer or contractor comes to mow or cultivate your field he will bypass these places even if they are not fenced off, because his machinery can't get in there and he hasn't the time to fuss about with nooks and crannies. These areas will fast become weed patches if left, so plant them with trees which will give useful shade for stock in the summer.

Soils

One of the main factors to take into consideration when fencing is the type of land or soil you will be working on. This can vary from one side of the farm to the other and from one side of a field to the other, and must be taken into account when planning your fields. For instance, on rocky or stony ground you might get an angle iron post in where a wooden post would not go, or it could be better just to go for electric fencing or replace a tumbled down wall or replant a hedge. These are the kinds of decisions you might have to make when planning your fences.

Public Rights of Way

It is important to maintain all fencing, gates and stiles where Public Rights of Way are found on your property, and to ensure that the route is 'way marked' to prevent trespass. It is very difficult to get the route of a footpath changed: I have seen many paths going across fields and crops when they could easily be re-routed round the edge. But that is officialdom, and it is almost impossible to alter their ways of thinking!

Once the field or land is ready it is time to mark with stakes where the straining posts are going and any new gateways. Straining posts for livestock wire should be about 50yds or metres apart (just a few yards shorter than the length of a roll of wire so you are always by a straining post when you come to the end of a roll) but if you are using high tensile plain wire these can be up to 100yds apart (see chapter 11, High Tensile Fencing). A fence is only as good as the straining posts so these need time and trouble taken over them.

Chapter 4   Clearing and Preparation

The Best Time for Fencing

Plan to get your fencing done during the winter and spring months when the ground is wet. The posts go in more easily than in dry weather when the ground is hard, particularly clay soils. If you fence in the summer or after a long dry period, you will find the stakes you put in become very sloppy when the ground gets wet again and will need to be knocked in a bit further. If you are working in very dry conditions you may need to water the post holes to soften the ground; fencing in these conditions is a nightmare.

Clearing back to the fencing line

This can be a lengthy process but a satisfying one as you see what you have accomplished. Most of the work can be done with a chain saw, a bow saw, loppers, a slasher, a bill hook and a spade.

It is usually brambles, gorse and blackthorn that creep out into a field and these must be cleared back to the original fencing line. There may be small trees to be felled and large thorn bushes to be trimmed so do this carefully and judiciously as, after all, the hedge will be providing cover and shelter for your animals. It may be necessary to shape the hedge and you might also consider having it laid. On larger acreages you might have to use a flail mower to get back to the original fencing line, but these do make a ghastly mess. I always feel slightly bothered by the removal of all this natural habitat, especially from the point of view of wild birds, but if it is done sympathetically the hedge will grow back and become an excellent nesting place once again in a couple of years.

If things are very overgrown you may come across all kinds of horrors such as sheets of tin, bedsteads, bottles, tin cans and yards of twine, and you may even uncover a ditch as you cut back. This will have to be cleaned out and it is best to get it done mechanically. Ask the driver of the ditcher to put the spoil as far into the field as possible to allow natural surface drainage back into the ditch. This will also ensure that you are not working in muddy conditions along the fencing line.

When you are clearing up you can keep any heavier wood (anything over 2.5" in diameter) for firewood and the rest can be burned in situ. Choose your site carefully as the brash can get very hot and scorch neighbouring trees and hedges. Watch out for overhead power lines as well. The result of a brash fire after a few months is always a good clump of nettles. Wood ash is excellent for the garden so it is well worth bagging it up to take home. If there is a ditch to be dug out, position the fire about 4yds out from the fencing line, and the spoil from the ditch can be spread on the site of the fire as well as in the field. Allow the spoil earth to dry and pick out any roots, stones or other debris then rotovate or harrow it and plant with a mixed field grass seed. Roll this in when dry otherwise the seed will stick to the roller. If there is no ditch, then just dig over the fire site after you've cleared it of ashes, and sow the area with mixed field grass seed.

When you have finished, walk along the ditch if you have one and look for any land drain exits. These are normally reddish clay pipes; the more modern ones are made of blue plastic. Clean out the ends of the pipes and if it's winter, take a note of how they run. They are normally about 22yds or metres apart and sometimes you'll find a holly bush in the hedge as a marker.

Old wire

Do not re-use this as it never pulls into shape and will leave you with bulges and odd holes here and there. More importantly, when put under tension it can break with nasty consequences, particularly if it is barbed wire. This can come coiling back at you and if this happens it is best to hit the ground face first and let the coil pass over you. Very often one sees coils of decent looking wire at farm sales, but don't be tempted to buy it as you don't know where it was cut when it was dismantled, and livestock wire is not that expensive anyway.

If you have old wire to dispose of, just roll it up tightly and flatten the roll by jumping on it. Take it down to your local tip or put it in the skip with the rest of the rubbish you have pulled out of the hedge. On one farm I once cleared out two whole skips of rubbish, all metal.

27

Getting an old stake out of the ground

Dig into the stake with your spade below ground level and lever it out while holding it upright. Nine times out of ten this works when the ground is soft and the stake is only in 14" to 20" (36cm to 50cm), although the suction of wet soil can make things difficult. With more stubborn cases you may have to use a crowbar and chain. Attach the chain to the stake at ground level then wrap the chain round the crowbar and knot it. Put the point of the crowbar on a length of wood and heave upwards. There is quite a knack to wrapping the chain round the crowbar, but the stake should come out with this method. Failing this, use the strength of a tractor and pull it out with that.

Digging into the stake below ground level.

Stake being levered up

Chapter 5 Problem Areas

Sharp changes in fencing direction

Try to avoid this if at all possible as any odd corners always become untidy. Of course the deviation may have been caused by a boundary change or a tree in the way, so the remedy is to put in a section of post and rails and create a box tensioner. The original fence is then re-attached to this diversion and tightened up.

Uneven or hilly ground and hollows

Where the ground is uneven you may have to dig it away for a short distance to maintain the correct level, or conversely, build it up using stones and soil. If there is a short distance between stakes where a lamb could push underneath, you could either loosely staple a length of rail to the bottom of the livestock wire or you could put in a couple of short stakes and nail one or two rails across them to overcome the problem.

Most people use high tensile plain wire in hilly areas because the ground is often stony, rocky or boggy. Livestock wire is impractical with very uneven ground, and there is always the fear of animals getting their heads stuck in the wire as well. Straining posts can be set up to 200yds (metres) apart, with intermediate straining posts where dips or mini valleys occur or where the incline changes. There can be a problem with straining posts in dips being pulled up and out when the wire is under tension, so these must be put in the ground very carefully using additional anchor stakes. It may be better to use posts and rails in dips.

Ditches

The fencing line across ditches remains the same but there will be a gap underneath where sheep can get out. The amount of water that flows along the ditch determines the type of fence used here, also you must bear in mind the fact that it may flood in winter. If it is shallow and the flow not great, then

Fencing round a wide angle using an anchor post.

Blocking a gap under a fence.

30

two stakes with rails across will do the job. If the ditch carries a lot of water you will have to construct a gate the same shape as the dip, made of rails. Drive in a stake each side of the water and fix a rail across then hang the gate on the rail with loops of wire or chain. When the ditch is in spate the rail gate will swing open with the flow and most of the debris will pass underneath.

In both cases the fencing area around the ditch must be kept clear of debris to stop the water from flooding the surrounding land.

Streams

The problem here is the changing level of the water from low in summer to spates in winter. You must also be aware that the fence construction must be very strong to prevent floods from tearing it down if it becomes blocked with debris. Make sure you only use plain wire in areas like this as barbed would catch more debris to add to the blockage.

Each situation is different, but most fences across streams involve a top-swing gate, usually metal which is lighter, for a wider span. Two good sized posts are positioned one each side of the stream. Dig them in and concrete them and you will probably also have to put leaners in on the downstream side. Next you will need a long piece of metal gas pipe with several metal lugs welded to it. Fasten this pipe across the stream to the posts each side using metal straps. The gate is then hung from chains attached to the lugs, and can swing freely as the water level rises. Debris is not so much of a problem on moorland; you tend to find large stones being moved downstream, and these may have to be shifted from time to time to ensure the gate closes properly. Branches, leaves and twigs tend to clog up streams in more low lying areas, and will need to be cleared as and when necessary.

Fencing down to a gate post.

Fencing across a ditch.

Fencing round a tree

Long stakes beside new ditch

32

A curving fence

This is best constructed as a single smooth curve rather than several angles forming a curve; it's much easier for a tractor to follow the former than the latter. These curves are found round ponds, lakes, streams and spinnies and can look very pleasing.

Mark out a line on the ground where the fence will be and set out the stakes accordingly, normally 2 to 3yds or metres apart. Each stake must have a leaner and a stop to hold the wire in place; without this the post will move when it is under tension. This type of fencing is more expensive from the point of view of both time and materials.

Curved fence

Chapter 6   Straining Posts, Leaners, Box Tensioners & Turning Posts

Post holes for straining posts

First mark where the post is to go. Most contractors use a tractor driven auger or thumper when they are putting in straining posts, but it's easy enough to do by hand although it does take longer. For a straining post 8" to 9" (20cms to 23cms) in diameter you need a hole about 12" to 14" (30cms to 36cms) square and 3ft to 4ft (92cms to 122cms) deep. Take off the turf and top soil and put them to one side then start to dig out the sub soil. I use a couple of empty plastic feed or fertilizer bags to put the soil on as this helps to keep everything tidy, particularly in the winter when the ground is often wet and muddy. No two holes are similar and of course sub soil structure varies enormously. Be prepared for stones, flint, shale, sand, chalk, clay or rock; put aside and burn any roots that you come across. Assuming you have no problems, you will find that you have to pull the deepest soil out by hand once you get down to a certain depth, or you could use a Shuv-holer, (a kind of two-handled spade) for the job. Check the depth and if all is well

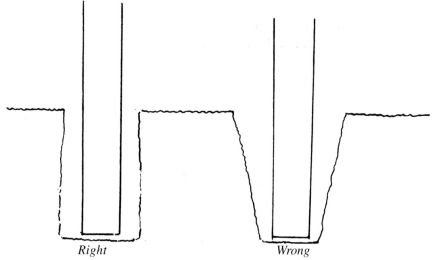

Right   *Wrong*
Right and wrong way to make a post hole.

34

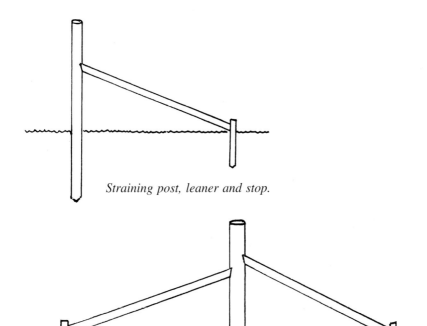

Straining post, leaner and stop.

Straining post with two leaners and stops.

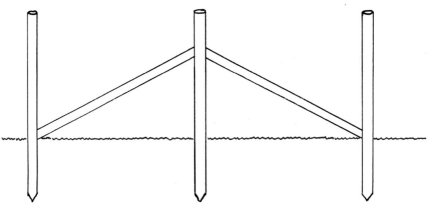

Straining post with two leaners and stakes as stops.

lift the post in. If your post is square position it in a corner of the hole with the help of your spade. If your post is round, choose your corner and dig out the sides a little so that it fits snugly into the curves. Check to see that it is upright with a long spirit level.

Most fencers consider it essential to fit a 'foot plate' to straining posts when using high tensile wire. For this you will need a piece of 4" x 2" (10cms x 5cms) or 3" x 2" (8cms x 5cms) about 12" to 14" (30cms to 36cms) long which you attach at right angles across the post a couple of inches up from the bottom. This prevents it from lifting out of the ground or turning in situ.

Sometimes it is advisable to put in a post that leans back slightly, although in line with the fence, to allow for possible movement when tightening at the straining post or along the fencing line.

The next stage involves back filling with the earth and stones that came out of the hole and it is very important to get this right. There are many different theories about it, some people saying not to use stones and others saying the opposite, but the real secret is to back fill gradually, ramming down really hard every 2" to 3" (5cms to 8cms). Keep checking with the spirit level too. When you have back filled half way the post should feel as solid as a rock; if it doesn't you are wasting your time! Some people put a brick or large stone at the bottom of the hole to wedge the post in, but it is the hard ramming that really counts. When all the sub soil is back filled there should be just enough room for the top soil and turf which you can heel in with your boot.

When digging your hole you may find that you can't get deeper than about two and a half feet (76cms) because you have hit solid rock or for some other reason. If this is the case you will have to concrete the post in. I don't really like to do this as wooden posts tend to rot more quickly than usual in this situation, but if need be it has to be done. Use a sand and gravel mix with cement, about 4 shovels to 1 of cement, and not too sloppy. Position your post and check it for uprightness with the spirit level. Add the concrete and tamp it well down with a piece of 2" x 2" to make sure it gets into every corner. Before finishing, check that the concrete is slightly higher in the centre round the bottom of the post to allow water to run away from it easily. You will probably need to support the post with a couple of fencing stakes nailed on to hold it in position until the concrete has dried; this should take 2 to 3 days. You can use quick drying concrete which is sold in packs but this is more expensive.

In some circumstances it may not be possible to put in a straining post in which case you will have to use a Box tensioner.

Stays, leaners etc.

These are used as buttresses to support the post and stop it from being pulled over when the wire is tensioned. There are several ways of doing this but I will describe the quickest and easiest method.

The stay or leaner should be at least 8ft (244cms) long otherwise there is a danger of the post being lifted up a few inches when the wire is tensioned, especially if the ground is soft or wet. The leaner should be attached a little over half way up the straining post, usually in line with the fence but sometimes at right angles to it. (See section on turning posts.) Cut a "vee" or notch about 2" (5cms) deep out of the post with a chain saw or bow saw. If you are also putting a leaner on the other side of the post, attach it about 6" (15cms) higher or lower than the first one so that the post is not weakened at the site of the two notches. Now shape one end of the leaner into a tongue to fit in the notch, making sure that the angles correspond with the "vee" and the ground. Once this is done the leaner can be pegged by a stop, usually a short length of stake knocked in vertically at the base or leaning slightly backwards. Sometimes the first stake of the fence acts as a stop in which case the end of the leaner will need to be cut to meet its vertical side. The sequence is: notch the post, cut the tongue of the leaner, position the stop, cut the leaner to meet the stop and bang the stop in. Nail through the stop to hold the leaner in place then drill and nail through the tongue on the leaner to hold that in place. It is best to use a drill to avoid the wood splitting which would look bad and weaken the joint. Some people staple a loop of wire round the join to hold it in place. It is important that it

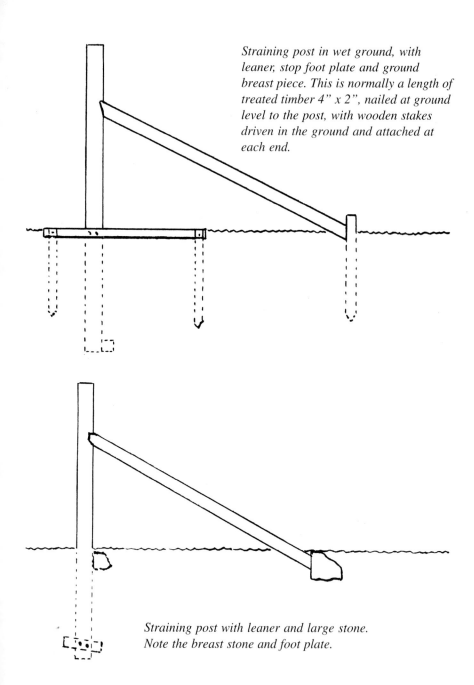

Straining post in wet ground, with leaner, stop foot plate and ground breast piece. This is normally a length of treated timber 4" x 2", nailed at ground level to the post, with wooden stakes driven in the ground and attached at each end.

Straining post with leaner and large stone. Note the breast stone and foot plate.

is as strong as possible so that if animals rub against it or the ground dries and moves, the leaner doesn't get knocked out of place or fall away.

If you are working on soft soil it is advisable to put a wooden foot plate or large stone against the end of the leaner and stones along either side where it goes into the ground. This can be further strengthened with extra stop stakes behind the foot plate or stone.

Leaner and post before notching.   *Leaner ready to go into the notch.*

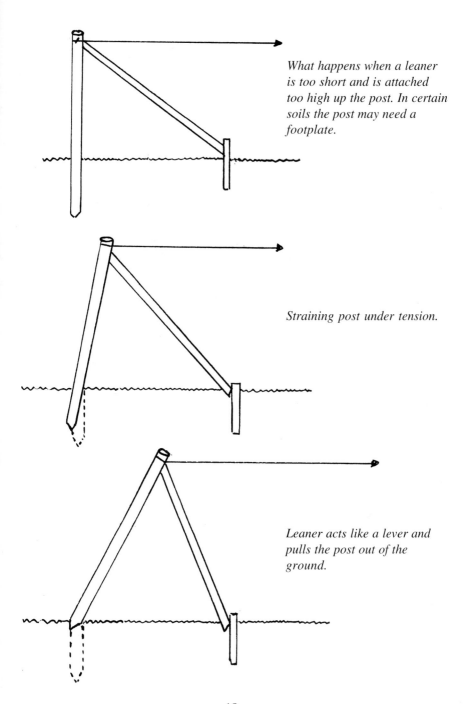

What happens when a leaner is too short and is attached too high up the post. In certain soils the post may need a footplate.

Straining post under tension.

Leaner acts like a lever and pulls the post out of the ground.

Post with notch for leaner.

Fencing past a telegraph pole

Post with triple leaners.

Box tensioners

These were first developed in New Zealand and can be very useful.

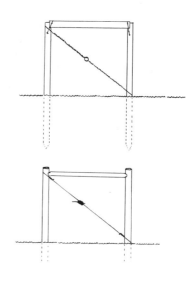

Box tensioners.

You will need three 4" to 5" (10cms to 13cms) diameter stakes. Knock two of them into the ground in line with the fence and approximately 5ft (152cms) apart, then cut a step out of the top of each one. Place the third stake so that it sits horizontally in these notches, and then nail it down. I prefer to use wire for this to give added strength. Another method is to chisel a 'vee' shaped notch out of the sides of the two upright posts facing each other and about 6" (16cms) down from the top. Shape the ends of the horizontal post to fit these notches and secure it in place with a nail through each post. The diagonal wire will pull everything up tight Next knock two staples halfway in near the top of one stake and another two staples halfway in near the ground on the other stake. Thread some mild sheet wire through these staples to make a continuous tight diagonal loop. The two ends should meet at the top of the post with each wire going under a staple, bending back on itself and being stapled again. At this stage hammer in the four original staples some more but not fully. Next, twist the wires really tight; to do this get a round metal pipe and inserting it at right angles between them, turn it end over end. Don't overdo it or the wires will snap. If you have a Gripple fastener use high tensile wire to thread through the four staples as above, then into the fastener and tighten it up with the tensioner tool. This will make a superb anchor for your fencing line, particularly on difficult ground.

A box tensioner.

Corner box tensioners for deer fencing.

43

Other forms of anchor for straining posts

These are nearly always posts, tree roots or trees. If a post is being used it must be in the ground at least two and a half feet (76cms) deep to do the job properly. Loop a length of wire round the straining post and the anchor post, put a couple of staples in both to hold the loop in place, then twist it tight using a round metal pipe. This is easy with the Gripple system; you need two lengths of wire, one attached firmly to the straining post, the other to the anchor post. Poke the wires into the Gripple and tighten them up with the tensioning tool then trim off any excess.

Tree roots can also be used like the anchor post. It is best not to use trees but if all else fails this is the way to do it. Never staple the straining wire directly to the tree. Instead get some 6" to 8" (15cms to 20cms) lengths of treated stake and staple these "noggins" to the straining wire. Then loop this bracelet of noggins round the trunk and pull it as tight as possible. Like this the wire will be held away from the tree, preventing it from becoming incorporated into the trunk and being a hazard to chainsaws for years to come.

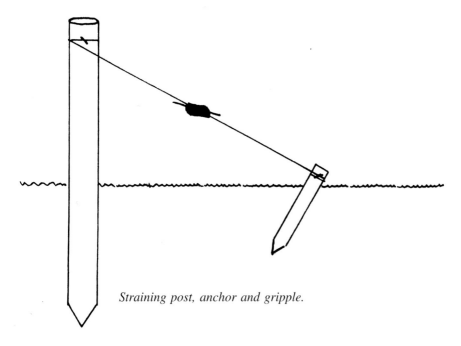

Straining post, anchor and gripple.

Wire embedded in tree trunk.

Noggins of wood protecting tree trunk from wire.

Turning posts

These are placed at points along the fence where it diverges from the original line. They are as strong as straining posts and are put in the ground the same way, sometimes with leaners, sometimes as part of a Box tensioner, sometimes by themselves. It is important to remember that under no circumstances do you put a leaner inside your field to support a turning post. Not only would it get in the way of farm machinery, but it could easily be dislodged by cows or sheep rubbing against it. A turning post is always situated inside the angle of the fence. Where there is only a slight deviation in the fencing line the turning post can usually cope by itself, but where there is a sharper change of direction, more support will be needed, either an anchor or a leaner.

Turning post

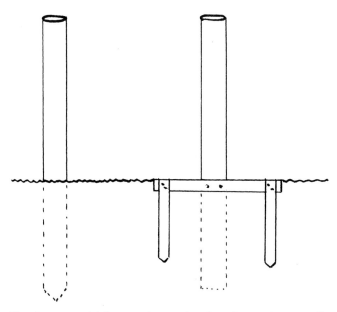

Turning post with breast plate and stakes, for use in wet soils.

Tractor driven post hole auger

47

Chapter 7 Stakes

There are various different types of stake. The common ones are round, half-round and square, the less common ones are cleft and mortised. Stakes do several jobs: they keep wire in line, they support it and they hold wires apart.

When you are fixing wire to stakes it is essential to avoid banging home the staples completely. This is because if the fence is hit by an animal the wire can move through the staples causing the fence to spring out and back, thus absorbing the blow. If the wire is stapled hard into each stake any impact would result in the fence stretching and sagging out of shape permanently. Of course the type of wire used would affect this to some extent.

If possible hand pick your stakes and discard bent or misshapen ones. Use peeled ones if you can find them as they are cheaper than the machine rounded stakes which have a tendency to snap if the wood is knotty. If your stakes are delivered and you have no chance to choose your own, you can cut down any misshapen ones and use them as stops for leaners.

Round stakes

These are the easiest to put in and come in various diameters. They are put into the ground from about 14" to 24" (36cms to 61cms) deep.

Half-round stakes

These make a useful fence, particularly where rails are used as there is more flat surface area to fix them to, but the stakes are not very easy to drive in. They also have a tendency to snap sometimes. If you are putting them in by hand you will need to lean the stake back from the fencing line and as it goes into the hole it straightens up and comes to the vertical. Another problem with this type of stake is keeping the flat surface parallel with the fencing line while it is being driven into the ground. If you can put these stakes in mechanically with a guide they work well.

Square stakes

These can be either pointed or flat ended and can be driven in with a thumper, part dug in and part driven in, or wholly dug in. They are normally put in by machine. Like half-round stakes, they have a nasty habit of twisting out of alignment, but it is quite easy to make a gadget to sort out this problem. You need a square metal frame slightly bigger than the size of the post, attached to a long handle. Slip the frame over the post and when it is down to ground level, pull on the handle and twist the post back into the correct alignment then ram the soil back round it.

Square stakes are used exclusively for rails, sometimes with plain or livestock wire as well.

Gadget for aligning square stakes.

Cleft stakes

Cleft stakes are normally made of oak these days and are often mortised as well to take cleft rails; the posts are always dug into the ground. This kind of fencing is very common in the south of England.

Mortised stakes

These are nearly always made of sawn oak or treated softwood with sawn rails to fit. Each stake is put into a vee shaped hole so that it can be leant backwards to receive the rails. Then it is pulled up to the vertical and the soil is rammed in tightly all round.

These last two methods of fencing are quite expensive because of the labour involved. They are normally found along driveways.

Putting in stakes

Once your straining and turning posts are in you will need to mark out where your fencing line will go using a taut string or wire. Next lay out your stakes 2 to 3 metres apart. If I am working on a short length of fence I pick up a bundle of 5 or 6 of them then pace out the distance and lay them at right angles to the line as I go. For longer distances I use a tractor and trailer or tractor box to carry the stakes. You will always find that you are left with an over- or under-sized gap once you have laid out all your stakes, so you will have to adjust the position of the last three or four. Some of the stakes may end up slightly closer or further apart than others but that won't matter. Next make a pilot hole about 18" (46cms) deep with a crowbar and put in the first stake then drop the Drival or thumper over the top and start to knock it in. If you don't make a pilot hole and the stake hits a root or stone it will move out of line or out of the vertical. Make sure it goes in upright and keep a check with a spirit level. If the stake is not going in straight you can correct it by pulling on the thumper as you bang it down; by the time you have done a dozen or so you will know when a stake 'feels' right!

Putting in a post with a Drival or thumper.

The next important thing is to make sure the stakes you put in end up all the same height. You can either use a stick as a guide or do what I do and use a button on my jacket or a pattern on my jumper as an indicator of the correct height; nothing looks worse than a row of stakes all at different levels. Some people would just take a saw to them but if you did this you would lose the impregnation of the wood treatment on the end of the stake. Occasionally it might be necessary to cut one down to size if you hit rock, but you will pick this up when putting in the pilot hole with the crowbar.

When the line is complete check that everything is vertical. If there are one or two out of line take a spade to the offending stakes and dig down on the side that they need to move over to. Pull them upright and ram the soil firmly back all round, then take up your marking string and move on to the next section.

Stakes along a fencing line.

Mechanical post hammer, Brown's.

Chapter 8   Attaching Wire to Posts

Remember, whichever type of wire you are using, you always put it on the livestock side of the post, except in exposed areas where you put it on the side facing the prevailing wind.

Livestock wire

This is like a type of large netting with different sizes of 'mesh' available for use with different kinds of stock.

Take your roll of livestock wire to the straining post, clip off the metal ties and remove the paper. Unroll a few yards of wire and anchor it by the post with a spade or crow bar then kick out the rest, keeping it parallel with the fencing line as you go. Once the roll is undone stand the wire up against the last straining post and secure it with a nail to keep it roughly in place. Pull the wire upright as you go back to the start, securing it with a 2" nail every 3 or 4 posts. When you get back to the beginning staple it to the first straining post. If the field slopes then the wire will not leave the post at right angles but will go parallel with the slope. Make sure the wire is about 2" (5cms) above the ground and use the instep of your boot as a guide.

All high tensile wire is 2.5mm but mild steel livestock wire has top and bottom strands which are thicker than the others; these will need three staples each to secure them to the straining posts, the intermediate ones will need two. High tensile wire is normally wrapped right round the straining posts and twisted back on itself. Once the beginning is secured, go down the line pulling the wire tight and moving the 2" nails where necessary so they don't impede the wire tensioning.

Joining wire

There are several ways of doing this. You can twist one end of wire into a loop and hook the other end into it and make a loop of that; an experienced fencer of 20 years recommends it as being the quickest and cheapest method.

Then there is the Gripple method; this has its advantages on uneven ground and allows you to tighten the top or bottom wires to gain the correct tension. Alternatively, if you are using high tensile wire, you can crimp it using a special sleeve.

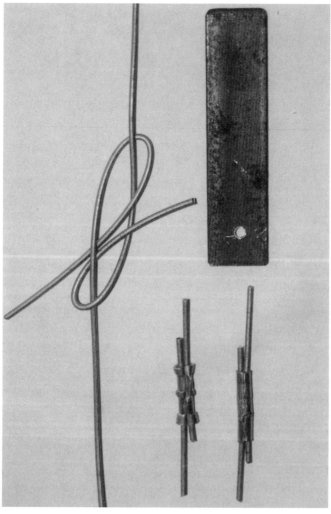

High tensile fencer's knot, wire bender, and two examples of wire crimped together.

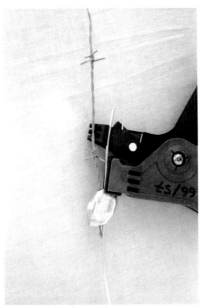

Gripple tensioner open.

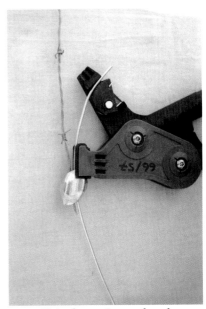

Gripple tensioner closed.

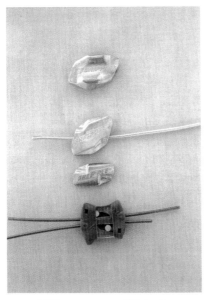

Different types of Gripple.

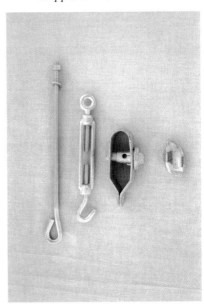

Eye bolt, bottle screw, radisseur and Gripple.

Gripple

If you have not come across this system before then you don't know what you have been missing! Apart from joining wire together, this clever device not only tensions but also holds wire under tension. I had not used this system until a friend of mine in Devon lent me his Gripple tensioning tool and a few Gripple joiners for me to try out. Before this I had always used radisseurs, bottle screws and eye bolts to tension wire, particularly mild steel wire which loses its tension after a while. I was amazed at the strength of the Gripple joiners. As they are made from zinc they don't rust; they are left permanently attached to the fence and will move posts when under tension if you are not careful.

The Gripple works on two high precision gear-tooth rollers set inside a small metal case or joiner. There are several sizes of Gripple to suit different diameters of wire. The wires are fed into the case from either end and can only go one way, so make sure everything is ready before you start because once your wires are in the Gripple there is no going back. If you need to, you can of course cut the wire either side, to release the Gripple, and then pull it out and start again.

Tensioning of wires can be achieved from either end of the Gripple. Open the tensioning tool as wide as possible and you will see that the wire gripper or cleat opens as well. Locate the joiner, with the wire in situ, into the special location point on the tool. Make sure that the wire is sitting in the teeth of the gripper or cleat then gently close the handles of the tool. The wire is pulled about 2" (5cms) every time you close the handles. This may not seem much but because of the gearing on the tool, you can pull up the wire about 1ft (30cms) with six flips of the wrist.

The Gripple will handle barbed wire as well as plain providing you remove the barbs from the wire that is going into the joiner. Attach some plain wire to the straining post and push the other end into the joiner in the opposite direction then pull up the barbed wire towards the post by means of the plain wire

Anyone who has wire fencing to put up or repair should consider this system, whether for permanent or electric fencing, plain or barbed wire or livestock wire.

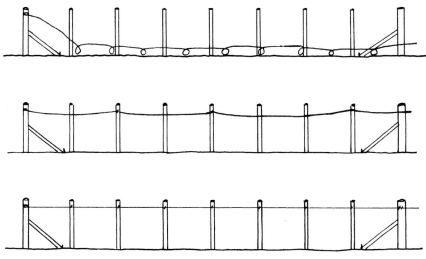

Stages in attaching wire to stakes.

Barbed and plain wire

You either like barbed wire or you don't use it at all. It's certainly not popular with a lot of horse owners, and some sheep owners feel the same, particularly those with long wool breeds which could easily get tangled up in the barbs.

Barbed wire is always put on at the end of the fencing operation. It comes on a wire or wooden reel with a central hole. Don't forget to wear gloves whenever you are working with it. You may be putting up a single strand or several strands of wire. Cut off the tie, bring the end round the straining post at the required height and twist it round itself then secure it with two staples. To unroll the wire you will need either a crowbar or a length of metal pipe about 3 to 4ft (92 to 122cms) long which you slide through the central holes in the reel of wire. This can be a one man operation but is better with two. Pick up the crow bar or pipe and walk along the fencing line with it, unreeling as you go. You have to walk backwards if you are doing it by yourself. When you reach the end unroll some extra then put your foot on this to anchor it before you cut it. If you don't hold it down the whole lot will coil back down the field as soon as it is severed. Pick up the end of the wire and twist it either clockwise or anti-clockwise to get rid of the coils then pull it as tight as possible. Put in some 4" nails at various places along the fencing line to hold up the barbed wire, and half bang in a few staples along the line as well, to act as a kind of brake should you over tension the wire. It's a good idea to stand on the opposite side of the post from where the wire is being attached just in case it breaks. Tension it slowly and carefully but don't overdo it. Using a block of wood or a measuring lath check that the strand is in the correct position on the stakes. Staple the strand to the stakes but don't hammer the staples home until you get to the straining post. Hammer each staple in firmly here, two for every strand, if possible across the barbs.

Plain wire attached to Monkey strainer.

Two rolls of livestock wire joined with Gripples.

Release the Monkey strainer and take it away then wrap the barbed wire round the post using a hammer. Cut the wire leaving enough so that you can twist it back round itself, making the fence secure and neat. If you have been using the Gripple, trim off any loose ends of wire and tidy up the working area. Always pick up any off-cuts of wire or nails, etc. and take them home to dispose of.

Short lengths of barbed wire can be tensioned with fencing pliers or bar strainers, but don't use this method with long lengths of wire or your fence will end up with tight stretches and saggy stretches after a couple of years.

Where there are Public Rights of Way the use of barbed wire on and around gates and stiles is prohibited. The barbs are quite easy to snip off and undo or you can use a piece of plastic water pipe cut lengthwise to slip over the wire. Because barbed wire is twisted it will stretch with time, so avoid clambering over barbed wire fences for this reason. They will need tightening occasionally and the Gripple is ideal for this job.

Plain wire

This is much easier to handle than barbed wire and comes in coils. There is always an end with a tab on it marking the starting point, but if you make a mistake and use the wrong end you will get in a terrible muddle! Once you have attached the right end to the straining post carefully unroll it a few coils at a time and walk down the length of the fence with it. Make sure you leave enough at the other end to tension it with then anchor the wire before you cut it to stop it coiling back down the field. Tape or wire up the rest of the coil to keep it tidy then pick up your cut end, make a 90 degree bend about 1ft (30cms) long to form a kind of handle and use this to unwind the wire and get rid of the coils. Attach the wire to the tensioning tool or Gripple and gradually tighten it, putting in a few staples or 2" nails along the fencing line to keep it in place and support the slack. When the wire is tensioned staple it firmly in two places onto the straining post then cut it leaving an end about 8" (20cms) long. Bend this back onto the staple, flatten it with a hammer then put another staple across it to hold it in place. Alternatively, you can pull the excess round the post and cut it leaving about 8" (20cms) which you twist round the tensioned wire with a wire bender or twister before snipping off any loose ends. If you are using the Gripple system, leave 4" when you are cutting off excess wire in case you need to retension it at any time.

Two methods of joining mild steel livestock wire.

Chapter 9   Tensioning Wire

Livestock Wire

For this job you need a livestock wire straining clamp, a tractor or other vehicle, and a tensioning tool known as a Monkey strainer. Once the livestock wire is clamped (see photographs) position the tractor or other vehicle in line with the fence. Anchor one end of the Monkey strainer to the tractor or vehicle and the other end to the livestock wire clamp. (Never try to tension with a vehicle as you could end up stretching the wire.) Pull the Monkey strainer chain tight by hand and tension the wire with the ratchet on the strainer. You will need to walk down the fence to check that the wire is not snagging on anything. Make sure that it roughly follows the contours of the ground; for hollows see the section on uneven ground. Go back to the Monkey strainer and tension again until the strainer can do no more then fasten the wire firmly to the straining post with two staples. Now slowly release the Monkey strainer and check to make sure the staples in the post are holding. If all is well remove the Monkey strainer then undo the straining clamp and take it off the fence.

Livestock wire straining clamp open

Livestock wire straining clamp attached to Monkey strainer.

There are two ways of finishing off. First, you can bend the wire back on itself across the post, stapling once more, then cutting it and twisting the end round the original strand. The other way is to simply wrap the wire round the post then cut the end and staple it.

Now you are ready to staple the wire to the stakes. Take a pocketful or small bucket of staples and work your way along the line making sure that you keep the wire the same distance from the tops of the stakes and the same distance from the ground, using the instep of your boot as a measurement. The top and bottom strands must be fastened to every post while the middle six can be fastened in threes to each alternate post (see diagram). This saves on costs. Always staple at an angle across the grain of

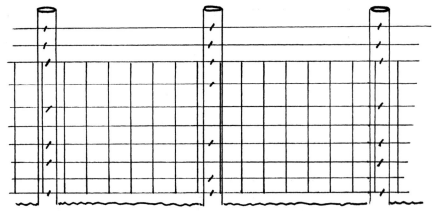

Wire stapled to stakes.

the wood, not vertically in line with it. When you are putting in your staples do not hammer them home but only three quarters of the way. There are three reasons for this: first, it will be easier if you need to tension the fence again at a later date, second, if a stake needs replacing you can take out the staples easily without damaging the wire and third, it allows for even tension along the length of the fence.

Tensioning Wire Round a Turning Post

This is achieved by taking the wire round the front or back of the post depending on the angle of the bend. If you are standing within a bend (a concave bend) then the wire goes round the back of the post on the side furthest away from you. If you are standing on the outside of a bend (a convex bend) then the wire passes round the side of the post nearest to you. You must ensure that the strands slide freely round the post and the verticals don't get caught and start bunching up together. Tighten up the wire as much as you can by hand, then staple all the wires to the post, knocking the staples in just three quarters of the way. Before the wire is tensioned slip another staple behind each strand so that the wire is held away from the post and can slide freely.

Box tensioner with Monkey strainer.

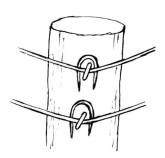

Straining wire round a post.

Tensioning Without a Tractor

This applies to using box tensioners, tree roots and trees. Always try to organise it so that your anchor point is in line with the fence, because tensioning round a bend can pull the straining post over. The anchor point on a box tensioner is the second post and the Monkey strainer is attached to this and to the chain on the livestock wire straining clamp. The wire is tightened up and when taut, stapled to the first post. Each wire is double stapled, the chain on the Monkey strainer is slackened and the strainer is taken off. The livestock wire straining clamp is removed and the extra wire at the end is tightened up using either fencing pliers or a bar strainer. Attach all the wires securely to the second post then trim them neatly. Where a tree root or tree in a hedge is used as an anchor you will need extra chain or thick rope to reach further. Attach one end of the Monkey strainer to this and the other to the straining clamp chains then tighten it all up with the ratchet. You may need to have several goes at this to take up the slack in the extra long anchor chain or rope. Once it is taut staple the wire to the straining post, using two staples on each strand. Release the Monkey strainer and undo the clamp then wrap the ends of the wire half way round the post. Staple them again and trim off the excess wire.

Bar strainer in use leaving hands free.

Fencing pliers straining short distances of wire.

Putting Up Light Netting or Chicken Wire

This comes in the form of plastic game netting or galvanized wire both of which stretch when tensioned. Unfortunately when galvanized wire is stretched it looses its shape which is why second-hand chicken wire is never much good when reused.

It is always best to put up these nettings with a strand of plain wire along the top and bottom. Once the plain wires have been tensioned, roll out the netting and, pulling it as tight as you can without distorting it, attach it to the stakes with lightly hammered in nails. The netting should hang vertically like a flat curtain. Now clip the top of the netting to the plain wire approximately every 4" to 6" (10cms to 15cms). Remove the nails supporting the netting from the top of the stakes, then gently tension it to the straining posts and staple it in place. Now clip the netting to the bottom wire. If you are using two different types of netting you will need to add another strand of plain wire at the point where they meet, and clip them both to it. This will make a good strong join. If you have netting 6ft (180cms) wide it is a good idea to run a strand of plain wire along about half way up to help keep it in shape and stop it from bagging.

Chicken wire hung on a nail and then clipped on with rings.

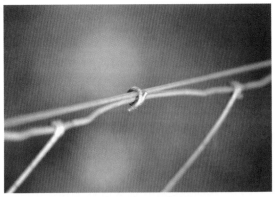

Ring clipped round wires.

Chapter 10   Post and Rails

These come in two kinds, the most common being sawn posts and rails, with the posts 5" x 3" (12.5cms x 7.5cms) and the rails 3.5" x 1.5" (7.5cms x 4cms). The other kind has half round posts about 5" (12.5cms) wide and half round rails about 4" to 5" (10cms to 12.5cms) wide. The rails are usually 12ft (360cms) long, and the posts 6ft (180cms) long.

A post puncher from Meade Machines.

The posts are normally driven into the ground by machine to save time and ensure that they go in square with the fencing line; if thumped in manually they will very often twist, (see section on square stakes) but modern post drivers have guides to prevent this. The posts need to be 28" to 30" (70cms) in the ground.

Mark the position of your fencing line with a taut string or twine and the post positions at 6ft (180cm) intervals. It is best not to go more than two posts ahead to ensure that the rails meet in the centre of each one. Decide on the height of the top rail and use a block of wood as a spacer when you fix the rails to the posts. A spirit level comes in handy here too. It should be relatively easy to keep your rail fencing in a straight line providing the ground is level or just has a gentle slope.

The challenge comes when the fencing line has to veer away from the original line for some reason or meets an incline or dip. At the point where the direction changes most contractors put in another post shoulder to shoulder

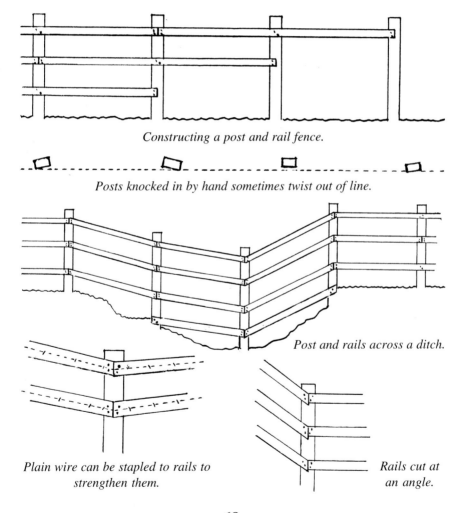

Constructing a post and rail fence.

Posts knocked in by hand sometimes twist out of line.

Post and rails across a ditch.

Plain wire can be stapled to rails to strengthen them.

Rails cut at an angle.

with the last one in the line. An alternative would be to saw and chisel out a rebate or notch to accommodate the rails at the new angle. When the fencing line dips or rises you will notice that the distances between the rails alters and the posts get nearer to each other. All the rail ends will have to be sawn at the correct angle to meet those at the end of the original fencing line. On uneven ground you may find it necessary to use longer posts and perhaps put in an extra rail to prevent livestock from creeping through.

Finally here are several points to remember: first, avoid bent, curved or knotty wood when selecting your rails, second, always fix the rails to the posts on the inside or stock-side of the fence, and third, if you stagger the places where the rails are fixed together you will avoid having all the joins on the same posts, thus making the fence stronger.

Post and rail fence.

Chapter 11 High Tensile Fencing

This type of fencing comes into its own over long distances and is usually put up by contractors, mainly because specialist tools have to be used; but this doesn't mean that a smallholder can't have this kind of fencing for shorter runs. A contractor will fence livestock wire up to 300m in one stretch, or plain wire (8 separate strands) up to 500m. This type of fencing is suitable for horses, cattle, sheep and deer, and is also used in Zoos.

High tensile fencing demands strong and well dug in straining posts, about 12" (24cms) in diameter. These need to be in the ground a minimum of 3.5ft (100cms) and more on lighter soils, always with leaners and sometimes box tensioners as well.

High tensile wire feels quite different from normal mild steel wire; it's very hard to bend and quite whippy. It comes in two basic forms, eight plain wire strands or livestock wire with 'mesh' of various sizes to prevent sheep from getting their heads stuck. Sometimes there is a combination of both, sometimes part or all is electrified. What you choose depends on the animals to be fenced in or out and/or the landowner's specification.

If you are dealing with uneven or hilly ground you should use the 8 strand wire. Once you have worked out the fencing line, avoiding any trees or boulders there may be, put in the straining and turning posts as well as some additional supporting posts on hillocks or in dips; these will all need leaners. You will have to fix spacers or droppers to your 8 strands every so often to hold the wires apart; these can be made of wood, wire or metal. Most people put stakes in 10m apart. The wire strands are all tied with a special knot at one end of the fence and strained at the other using either a Gripple or a radisseur. They can be tightened periodically when necessary.

High tensile livestock wire is used on mainly level ground. The straining posts are put in about 200m apart and the stakes can be about 8m apart, although the closer the stakes are the stronger the fence is, so 4 to 6m would be preferable. These stakes should be 5ft 6" (168cms) long. Stakes 6ft (183cms) or longer might be needed for soft or wet ground or for crossing

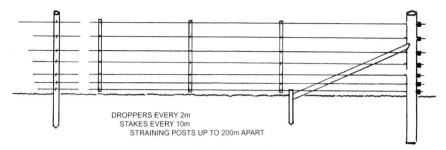

DROPPERS EVERY 2m
STAKES EVERY 10m
STRAINING POSTS UP TO 200m APART

High tensile plain wire fencing.

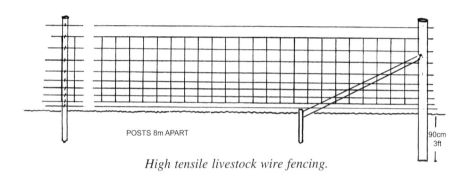

POSTS 8m APART

90cm
3ft

High tensile livestock wire fencing.

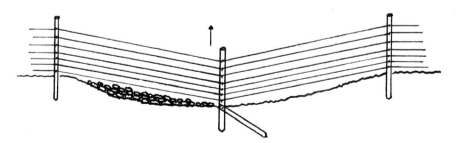

High tensile plain wire fencing across uneven ground.

71

High tensile plain wire with radisseurs.

High tensile fencing with two plain wires.

High tensile fencing with two electrified plain wires.

steep terrain. It is advisable to add some stout 9" (15cm) posts every 50m to support the wire.

Once the posts and stakes are in the ground take a 100m roll of livestock wire to each straining post. Take care to wear gloves and mind your fingers when you are cutting the bands on the rolls as they are very tightly bound and can spring open quickly. Undo about 5m of wire and wrap the end round the straining post, securing it in several places with staples. (Wrapping the wire round the post gives it extra grip so you are not relying on the staples alone.) Do the same with the roll of wire at the next straining post and when that is also secured, unroll both lots of wire towards each other so that they should meet in the middle.

Strain the two lengths of wire towards each other, using a livestock wire straining clamp on each roll and a Monkey strainer top and bottom on the two ends of wire in the middle. Cut off any surplus wire leaving enough to join the two stretches together. You can do this with a Gripple or a crimping sleeve. Either way you need a Gripple tensioning tool or a tool to swage (or squeeze) the crimp sleeve onto the wire. Once this has been done you can take off the Monkey strainers and clamps, then go along the fence stapling the wire to the posts and stakes.

Many people putting up this type of fencing add one or two strands of barbed or plain wire along the top. These are attached to the straining post at one end and tensioned at the other end with a radisseur or Gripple. You will have to temporarily support the barbed wire in position with 4" nails to prevent it from snagging while it is being strained.

High tensile livestock wire fencing, note different mesh sizes.

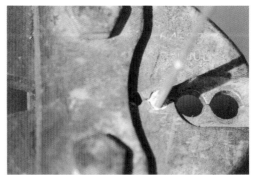

Crimping tool

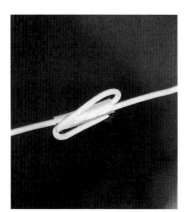

Two lengths or wire crimped together.

74

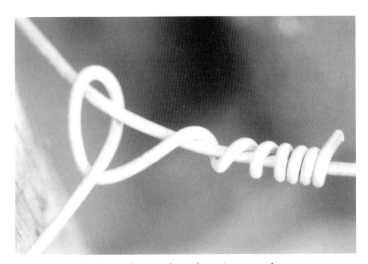

High tensile wire knot for tying round posts.

High tensile livestock wire is always wrapped round the post.

Chapter 12   Gates

Location of gates is important, not only for vehicular access, but also for movement of stock.

Try to position a gateway on a dry, level part of the field towards a corner if possible. If the access is wet, driving in with a tractor will eventually cause deep ruts and you may have trouble closing the gate. This can be overcome in the summer months by removing the top soil between the gate posts and either side, putting down some Terram (permeable membrane) and then covering everything with hardcore or stones. Raising the gate to avoid the ruts can create problems with lambs getting out.

When you are driving stock out of your field you will appreciate the sense of positioning the gateway near a corner. In fact stock quickly learn where the gate is and come to associate it with a move to fresh pasture; you will notice them gathering round the gate when they begin to run short of grass, although stock new to a field can be extraordinarily stupid.

Roadside gates should open into the field, and it may be necessary to make a turn-in area if the road is a busy one. This allows you to pull off to open the gate and close it on leaving before turning out onto the road again.

Where a gate is positioned on sloping ground it may be necessary to either dig out the ground round the gate area to make a flat approach, or to nail or bolt a rail under the gate parallel with the ground to stop lambs from escaping. This can also be done with strong twine to form a swinging rail under the gate.

Fencing either side of gates

Most people don't like to use the gate post as a wire tensioner post but prefer to have a separate post for this and put in wooden rails in between. This is a good idea as it makes the gate more visible for livestock, and prevents injury to cattle from barbed wire if they all try to barge through a gateway together. If you are in hunting country then the rails next to the gate make an opportunity for a jump. Make sure it is solidly constructed; one method is to fix a length of telegraph pole about 20ft or 7m long across the top at a height of about 3.5ft or just over 1m with a wooden rail underneath.

Gate post holes

Once the location of the gate is established and you have decided which way it will open, you can make a start by marking where the gate post is going to be, then the digging can begin. There are three main ways of doing this: manually, or with a mechanical auger or with a narrow bucket on a mechanical digger. The lighter the soil the deeper the hole you will need. On light or clay soils you will need to go down 3.5 to 4ft (107 to 122cms), on stony or rocky ground just go as deep as you can. If you use an auger you will have to shape the hole so that the post fits snugly into the 'corner' nearest the gateway. You may need a short plank to help manoeuvre the post and stop it from damaging the edges of the hole as it goes in. Now check for uprightness with a long spirit level. The top of the gate post

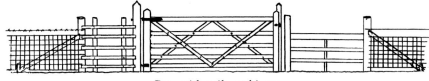

Gate with rails and jump.

should be at least 1ft (30cms) above the top of the gate. Start to gradually back fill with stones and sub-soil, leaving out any cut roots, turf or top soil. If the hole fills with water empty it out with a small tin and drop the post in quickly then back fill with stones and earth. Ram home the back fill really hard and continue to add soil and compact it as solidly as you can. Don't forget to keep an eye on the spirit level as you go. By the time you are halfway up, the post should feel as solid as a rock. Continue back filling and compacting until you reach the top, then add the soil and turf.

To cut down on mess and keep the job as tidy as possible, I usually put the post hole soil onto a couple of plastic bags until I need it.

On rocky ground you may well have to set a gate post in concrete. If this is the case you will have to increase the size of the post hole. You will need two or three barrow loads of concrete at 4 to 1, that is 4 shovelfuls of mixed sand and gravel to 1 shovelful of cement. Leave the post for two to four

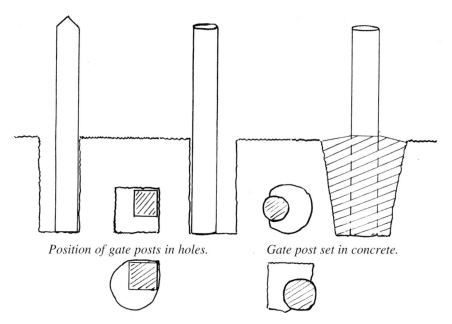

Position of gate posts in holes.   *Gate post set in concrete.*

days to allow the concrete to set before hanging the gate. Alternatively you could use quick drying concrete.

Wooden gates and metal gates

Personally I always feel that wooden gates look more natural and attractive than metal ones and they have a certain amount of bounce to them if caught by a machine. They are heavier than metal gates and will sag if not properly made. The life span should be 50 to 70 years depending on the wood used and the treatment process involved.

Metal gates are economical and light but they do bend and are no use in coastal areas. Having said that, there are a lot of old metal gates in Cornwall, and the ones that do last are the old blacksmith made wrought iron ones.

Putting on the hinges

Slide the top hinge bands over the gate and along the top rail then knock them up tight with a lump hammer. Now drill out the holes for the bolts; these are normally five eighths of an inch. Take great care to ensure that they line up

Ramming soil and stones into post hole.

Drilling holes for gate hooks.

Gate post nearly ready.

Drilling holes for gate hooks. Note the spirit level.

79

exactly with the holes in the hinge bands each side; this is sometimes quite tricky. Knock the bolts through and tighten them up. The bottom hinge normally has one bolt hole with a screw hole each side of it. It should be about 9" (23cms) up from the bottom of the heel but this can be adjusted if you are putting a new gate onto old hooks. Drill a hole, knock the bolt through, then tighten it up and put the screws in. Now you are ready to hang your gate.

The process with a metal gate is much simpler as it incorporates sliding eye bolt hinges which can be adjusted up and down or in and out. The eye bolts are usually slack if used with old hooks which means that the metal gate never fits quite as well. You may also find you have to change the fastening system.

Square posts or round posts

Square posts win when it comes to looks, round posts when it comes to ease of hanging the gate. With square posts you may come across the problem of having to bore diagonally through them, whereas with round ones the hooks can go in anywhere and will always pass through the middle.

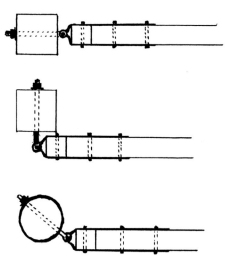

Different positions of hooks on gate posts.

Fixing hinge onto gate.　　　　　　*First step in hanging gate.*

Second step, lift the hinge end of the gate. Slide the gate across to the post and drop over the hooks.

81

Wood or metal posts

For years wood has been used traditionally for field posts and metal for around the farmyard, but these days you see metal posts everywhere. Some people use metal posts and gates for security and you frequently see these alongside main roads. They normally have the gate hooks welded to the post.

Hanging the gate

Once the gate post is in and set you are ready to offer up the gate, complete with hinges, to the post. You have a choice of three positions in which the gate hooks can be fixed into the gatepost: the side of the post facing into the gateway or one of the two sides at right angles to this. If you fix your hooks on the inside face of the post the gate will open both ways, if you choose one of the other two sides, the gate will only open one way. Get the gate into the right position against the gate post and support it on some blocks of wood with a couple of stakes to hold it upright. Make sure there is enough clearance underneath so it will open properly but not too much so that lambs will creep out. Check that the gate is vertical and level then mark a line on the gate post just under each hinge. Once this is done you can remove the gate and lay it on the ground nearby. If you are using a brace and bit you may not have enough room to drill out the bottom hook hole but you can get round this by digging out some soil as a temporary measure. You won't have this problem if you are using an electric hand drill. Drill the holes, positioning them on the lines you have marked and making sure that the top one is vertically above the bottom one. The size of augur is 22mm. It is very important that the hooks go in horizontally and pointing up vertically at right angles so that the gate swings properly. You may find that the gate post is not quite vertical in which case you will have to change the position of the bottom hook. Bang it in with a lump hammer and use an adjustable spanner to ensure that it is horizontal.

The top hook hole goes straight through the post and the hook is tapped in and through. Make sure it is vertical then lubricate it and the threads poking

Flange hooks.

Hinges set too far from the gate hooks. This allows lambs a way through.

Gate hooks badly knocked in and leaning towards the gate.

Latch and chain securing gate.

out of the other side of the post with tractor grease before attaching a large washer and nut to the threads. The bottom hook hole is drilled half the length of the hook which is then tapped in until tight; again, make sure it is vertical before you lubricate it. You need about 3" (8cms) of hook poking out of the post top and bottom. Tighten up the washer and nut on the top hook a little then you are ready to offer up the gate.

Here is a simple method of doing this if you are by yourself. Manoeuvre the gate into an upright position near the gate post then prop up the head (opening end) on several lengths of thick plank running parallel underneath. Supporting the gate vertically, walk along it and lift up the hinge end then slide it along the planks towards the hooks. Drop the hinges over the hooks, adjusting as necessary. You may have to carefully knock in the bottom one a little with a sledge hammer or take up the slack on the top hook with the nut and washer. Put the spirit level on the top rail of the gate to check the result. Remember how the forces of the gate work: the top hook is being pulled by the gate, the bottom one is being pushed back by it.

If you are hanging a wooden gate longer than 12ft (366cms) you will need two people; it would be far too heavy for one.

Some people have a problem with gates being stolen. To prevent this you can hang your gate with the top hook upside down but you will need two people to do it. Once the holes are drilled in the gate post, offer up the gate in the open position, that is at right angles to the gateway, with the gate heel (the end where the hinges are) propped up on some blocks of wood and the other person at the head of the gate steadying it vertically. Have the top hook ready, it's not yet in the gate post. Hook it into the top hinge, adjust the blocks so that the top hole lines up with the end of the hook, and start to tap it in with a lump hammer. While you are doing this, introduce the bottom hook into the bottom hinge and into the hole and tap that in as well. The hooks will gradually settle into position, you can bang the bottom one in firmly and the top one can then be used to level the gate. Alternatively you could use flange hooks with coach bolts.

Fitting a new gate to existing posts

When you are replacing an old gate with a new one try to salvage the old hinge bands because modern hinges may well not fit the old blacksmith made hooks. The top hinge band may be narrower or wider than the new gate so you will have to chisel out room for the band or put in some packing material so that it fits. The bolts will be no good so use new ones. When you have fixed the top hinge, carefully measure the distance between it and the bottom one. This is vital so double check your measurement before you fit the bottom hinge. Grease the old hooks when you have done this then offer the gate up to the post. Rest the head of the gate on a flat log or thick plank, slide the gate upright towards the hooks and you should find that everything marries up and you can drop the hinges over the hooks. Take away the log or plank and see if the gate swings well. Sometimes the measurements of the distances between the hinges are not quite accurate enough. If this is the case you can use washers to pack the top or bottom hinges and make the necessary adjustments.

Top gate hook reversed as an anti-theft measure.

85

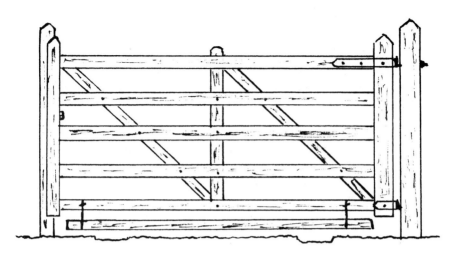

Gate with swinging rail underneath.

Chapter 13   Electric fencing

If you have not used electric fencing before or are unsure of any particular aspect of its use, you must seek professional advice. Electricity in the wrong hands is potentially lethal and you could kill your livestock and/or seriously harm yourself if you don't know what you are doing.

Today, when returns from farming are so poor, a lot of landowners resort to the cheapest kinds of fencing. Traditionally the old metal bedstead, sheet of corrugated iron or wooden pallet would have blocked up the hole in the hedge; nowadays electric fencing is seen as a cheap and permanent solution. There are several different kinds to choose from: plain wire, stranded wire, poly wire (a braided mixture of wire and polythene, string or cable), tape or netting. This is held in place by wooden posts with insulators or one of the many kinds of metal or polyposts, and secured by a range of joiners, connectors and tensioners.

All electric fences need an energiser. These can be powered by mains electricity or batteries which can be topped up using solar power, wind power or a mains source. An energiser converts a consistent electric current in a metered high voltage pulse, which on some units produces a clicking noise, and gives a shock if earthed. These energisers use between 15 and 75 watts, about the same as an electric light bulb.

Which is the best kind of energiser to buy? It's always advisable to seek professional advice on this as the answer will depend on a number of things: the power source the energiser uses (mains or battery), which kind of stock you are fencing in or out, the length of fence together with the number of electric lines needed, and the type of fence i.e. tape, wire or netting. It's a good idea to get an energiser with a slightly higher output than you need at the time in case you decide to add to your fencing lines in future.

Electric fencing is only efficient if it is properly earthed. For the system to work the electric pulses should pass along the tape, wire or netting, insulated from the ground by poly posts or insulators. In the case of netting the bottom line is dead as it does not carry electricity. When livestock comes in contact with the fence the current is earthed and the animal or bird gets a shock; but in order for this to be effective, there must be a proper metal earth-post or stake from the energizer into the ground to complete the electrical circuit. There are several different earthing systems available.

When you are introducing stock for the first time to a field with an electric fence, always do so in daylight with the electric power switched on; never do it at night. It is better to hold the animals up in a barn or secure paddock and wait till the morning before putting them into their new field. Once they have become acquainted with the fencing and have had a shock they will realise that the tape, wire or netting is not to be touched and will keep away from it. Certain animals like cows quickly learn to respect a single line of wire, sometimes even with the electricity off, whereas others like sheep will always keep trying their luck!

There are several important safety factors to consider if you have overhead mains electricity or telephone lines crossing your land. You must never run an electric fence along parallel beneath them; the fence can safely cross under these wires at right angles but must not be over 2m high (deer fencing). Never use more than one energizer on the same fencing line, and if you have two separate fences, make sure they are at least 3yds (3m) apart.

Permanent electric fences need to be regularly maintained and kept clear of twigs, branches or long grass which would short the system. You will need to spray any grass or vegetation under the fence and keep a clear line. However, if you are using an electric fence as a temporary barrier, for strip grazing for instance, make sure you use a powerful energizer to prevent loss of current in long grass as you won't be spraying under the fence in these circumstances. It is a good idea to use a "Night Light" to keep a visual check on your fence: as long as the fence is working properly the light flashes on and off. If the current is cut for any reason the light stops flashing so it's very easy to see immediately if there is anything wrong.

Apart from chainsaws, energisers are among the most commonly stolen items in the countryside so you must be careful to hide yours from public view or secure them in a metal box. If you have to put an electric fence anywhere near a Public Right of Way you must also attach an appropriate warning sign.

We follow with a description of the various types of non-electric and electric fencing suitable for different types of livestock.

Horses behind electric fence

Chapter 14   Types of Fencing

Horses

The important thing to remember when fencing for horses is to make the fence as visible as possible, particularly if there are no hedges, walls or trees adjacent to it, so always fix some rails or electric banding along the top. Horses can actually subject fences to quite a lot of wear and tear by rubbing and pushing against them, and stretching over them to reach grass on the other side. They will jump them, given half a chance, and bite or chew them, often a sign of boredom. Rather than have barbed wire most people use a single strand of electric wire to overcome these problems.

Non-electric fencing

The height of the fence and size and length of stakes and posts used will vary according to the size of the horses or ponies you keep. Horse fencing is the most expensive of all because of its construction which is why many owners use electric fencing; but although this works well it should never be used as a boundary fence, particularly where a road passes nearby. There have been many cases of horses bolting because of low flying aircraft, and a loose horse is obviously a serious hazard on a road. This leads to another point: try to round off the

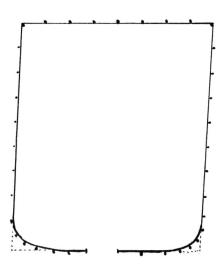

Rounded corners of a horse paddock at the bottom of a slope

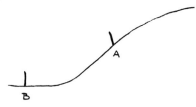

Fencing on a hillside at point 'A' could be a problem. Better to fence at point 'B'.

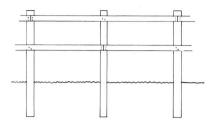

Dividing post and rail fence.

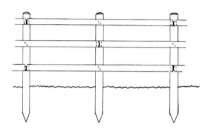

Boundary post and rail fence.

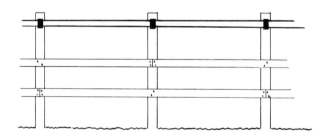

Post and rail fence topped with electric tape.

corners at the bottom of your horse's field. A galloping horse often does not brake in time and could get into trouble if it ran along a fence and into a corner, whereas if it can follow the barrier round a curve it will run out of the corner safely. Fencing across hillsides can also pose problems because if a fence is at a lower level a horse will often think it can jump over it.

91

Dividing fence

Boundary fence.

Half round post and rail fence.

92

Electric fencing

Most people today use electric tape as a fencing barrier, not only to divide fields but as a permanent fence, because it is extremely visible and very safe. Tape is not always the best choice though, because it tends to flap, stretch and break if used in exposed areas, so in this situation you should use electric cable instead. Electric wire is used in conjunction with wooden fences to prevent rubbing and crib biting. The height of the fencing will depend on the size and temperament of the horses or ponies concerned, and there are different kinds of tensioners and joiners for the tapes, cables or wires to keep the fence taut.

Insulator for electric tape

Electric tape fence

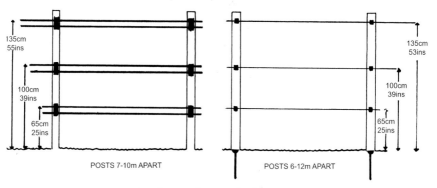

Electric fencing for horses.

93

Cattle
Non-electric fencing

Cows do not cause many problems unless there are bulls about, or they are short of food or water. Bullocks can do some damage, especially when they have just been let out after a winter indoors or when they are being pestered by insects. Cattle will always make a bee-line for fencing under shady trees, and will often barge into it or rub against it to rid themselves of flies. This could easily cause damage as the posts and stakes under trees are often not as deep in the ground as they should be owing to the presence of tree roots, so this is something you should be aware of.

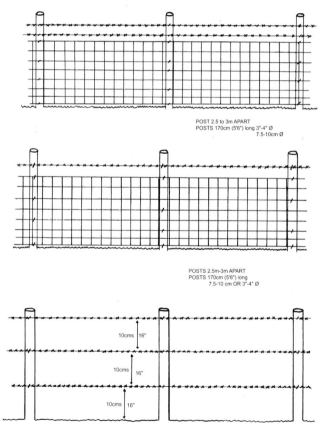

POST 2.5 to 3m APART
POSTS 170cm (5'6") long 3"-4" Ø
7.5-10cm Ø

POSTS 2.5m-3m APART
POSTS 170cm (5'6") long
7.5-10 cm OR 3"-4" Ø

10cms · 16"

10cms · 16"

10cms · 16"

Non-electric fencing for cattle.

94

Electric fencing

Cattle seem to adjust well to electric fencing and learn to avoid wire or tape if they have been 'stung' a few times. (This is usually the case even if the power is not switched on, but don't rely on it!) So the requirements for cattle are really quite straightforward. A single wire can be used very successfully as a permanent or temporary barrier, although you may need to add an extra wire if there are calves. Long horned cattle can be very destructive with livestock fencing as they can lift a length out of the ground with a flick of a horn. Electric wire fencing comes into its own with these breeds.

Cattle behind electric fence.

95

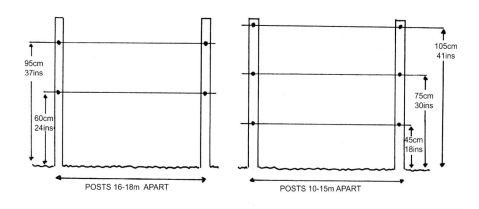

95cm
37ins

60cm
24ins

POSTS 16-18m APART

105cm
41ins

75cm
30ins

45cm
18ins

POSTS 10-15m APART

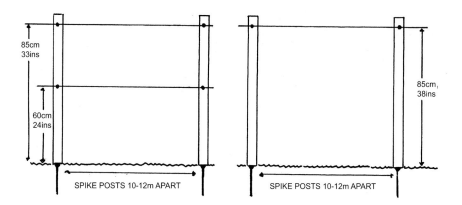

85cm
33ins

60cm
24ins

SPIKE POSTS 10-12m APART

85cm
38ins

SPIKE POSTS 10-12m APART

Electric fencing for cattle.

Sheep
Non-electric fencing

There is an old saying about sheep: they have only two aims in life, to get out or to die! Certainly the use of livestock wire (pig wire or an American woven wire) has made the containment of sheep much easier, but it does have some drawbacks, especially with certain horned breeds and lambs. You can normally overcome these problems however, by using single strands of high tensile wire fencing.

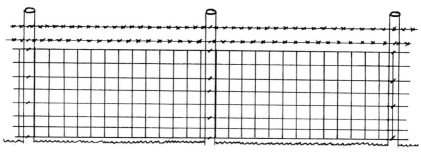

POST 2.5 to 3m APART
POSTS 170cm (5'6") long 3"-4" Ø
7.5-10cm Ø

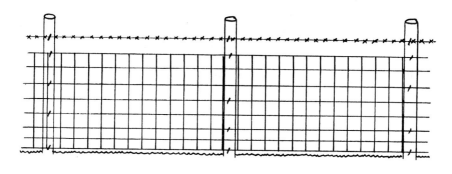

POSTS 2.5m-3m APART
POSTS 170cm (5'6") long
7.5-10 cm OR 3"-4" Ø

Non-electric fencing for sheep.

Electric fencing

Sheep can be a problem as their wool insulates them from electric shocks so they need more wire or netting to bring their faces or ears into contact with the fence. Netting should never be used if you have young horned breeds of sheep, and if your field is uneven you must make sure there are no gaps where adventurous lambs could squeeze underneath.

Sheep behind electric netting

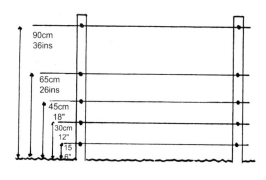

POSTS 20m APART, WITH
SPIKE POSTS EVERY 10m

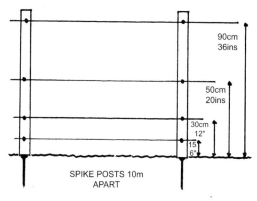

SPIKE POSTS 10m
APART

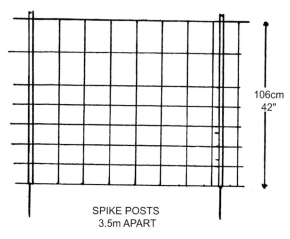

SPIKE POSTS
3.5m APART

Electric fencing for sheep

99

Goats and llamas

Non-electric fencing

This type of fencing is quite similar to that used for sheep except that this has two strands of plain wire or a rail and one strand of wire along the top. Never use barbed wire; goats are jumpers and if there is a shelter or bale near the fence to tempt them, they will be over.

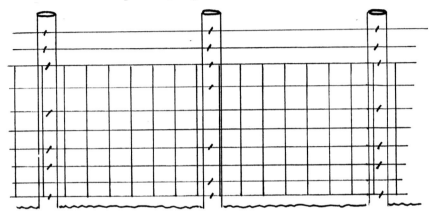

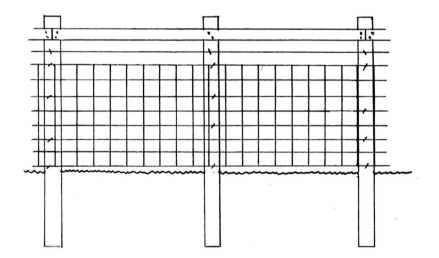

Non-electric fencing suitable for goats and llamas.

Electric fencing

Goats

Goats are normally rather intelligent and soon learn about electric fences, although most small goat keepers don't use them.

Llamas

Because llamas, alpacas and vicunas are valuable animals most owners use traditional secure wooden fencing rather than risk their stock getting out during a possible power cut. There are reports of camelids being somewhat impervious to electric fences and even chewing them when the power is off!

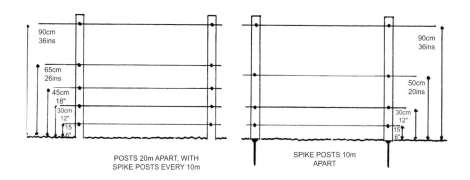

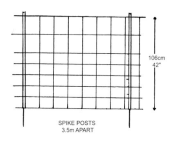

Electric fencing for goats and llamas

Deer
Non-electric fencing

As deer can leap considerable heights, you will need to use 6ft (1.90m) high tensile livestock wire with large straining posts or box tensioners at the ends. If they are frightened, deer bounce quite harmlessly off this fencing without doing themselves any damage.

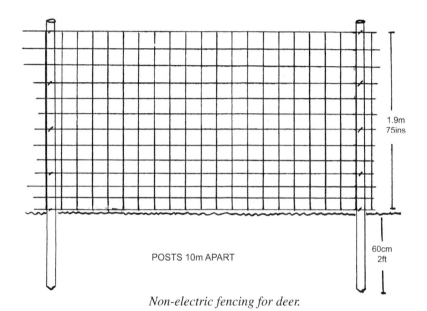

1.9m
75ins

60cm
2ft

POSTS 10m APART

Non-electric fencing for deer.

1.9m
75ins

90cm
3ft

Corner section of high tensile deer fencing.

1.9m high deer fencing.

This very old fence round the park at Charlecote near Stratford-on-Avon contains a large herd of fallow deer.

This is the modern equivalent of the above.

Electric fencing

Electric fencing is used not only to keep deer in but also to keep wild ones out of young plantations. In some cases a double line of fencing is required to prevent deer from leaping over. Braided poly wire or stranded wire is normally used on poly posts or wooden stakes with insulators, in these circumstances.

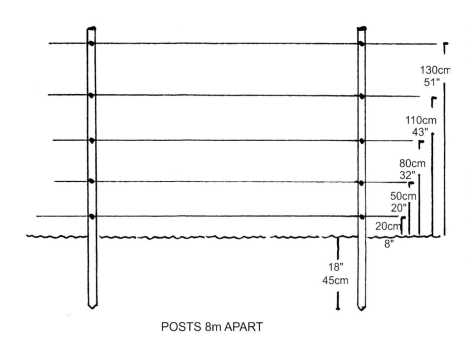

POSTS 8m APART

Electric fencing for deer.

Pigs
Non-electric fencing

Free range pigs are normally contained with one or two strands of electric wire. I have included a permanent fence which works well where there are pigs on view to the public. Note the barbed wire at ground level to prevent pigs getting their snouts underneath, because once they manage this it's not long before they break out.

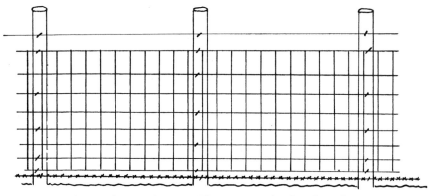

Non-electric fencing for pigs. The posts need to be about 2m apart.

Electric fencing

With the increase in organic pig meat production and welfare codes, more and more pigs are being kept out of doors and are contained by electric fencing. Pigs are extremely sensitive to electric fences and will not even cross them if they are laid flat on the ground. Unlike people on the Continent, we are not usually troubled by wild boar in this country, except nowadays in a few areas, but if you do have this problem you will need to put up a double line of electric fencing to keep your domestic stock apart from the wild animals.

Pigs behind electric fence.

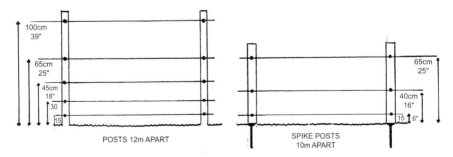

Electric fencing for pigs.

Rabbits
Non-electric fencing

For years people kept rabbits out by using 4ft (120cms) x 1" (2.5cms) wire netting. It is also used by the Forestry Commission on large plantations, although it is being replaced in some areas by tree guards as the cost of the wire increases. To install it you need to dig 1ft (30cms) of the netting into the ground and bury it. The Forestry Commission uses a single furrow plough along the fencing line, then 1ft of the netting is laid in the trench and the soil pushed back on top. This works well if you have light or clay soil, but a small digger or trenching machine would be better on stony ground.

While 3ft high fencing will normally keep rabbits out, it won't if there is a great drift of snow piled up against it! This can happen quite easily if the wind is in a certain direction, so be aware of this possibility when siting your fence.

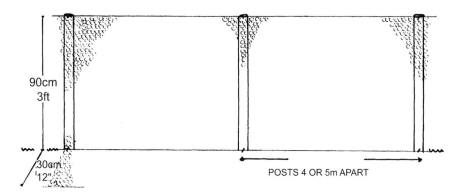

Non-electric rabbit proof fencing.

Electric fencing

Today electric fencing is used to keep rabbits off crops. There are two kinds of fence available, four single strands of wire, or netting. Both must be put up so that the fence slants towards the rabbits at an angle of 45 degrees. The four strands of wire are held in place by either plastic posts, composite posts or wooden posts and insulators.

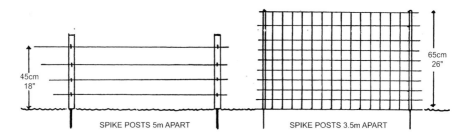

Types of rabbit proof electric fencing.

Rabbit and deer proof fencing round a new plantation.

109

Electric fencing for rabbits

Hares

Although hares are not nearly as numerous as rabbits, they can occasionally be a nuisance in very cold weather when they might nibble young fruit trees. Unfortunately a rabbit fence will not keep them out as they can easily leap over a 3ft high barrier so there is very little you can do about them.

Snow

To prevent snow drifting onto your land from neighbouring roads use either plastic 'Tensar' netting or chestnut paling with stakes every 2 to 3m. This can be rolled up in the Spring after the snowy season has passed. In some areas of high snowfall drifts can pile up against fences making ramps where sheep can get out, so be aware of this and move stock when necessary.

Poultry and Waterfowl

Non-electric Fencing

There are two basic designs of fox proof fencing with many variations.

A)   A 6ft (180cm) wire fence with 2ft (50cm) overhang facing outwards.

B)   A 6ft to 8ft (180cm to 240cm) fence with polythene overhead netting.

A) The posts can be made of 2"x 2" (5cm x 5cm) angle iron 8.5 to 9ft (250 to 270cm) long, or treated wood 8 to 9ft (240 to 270cm) long, 3 to 4" (8 to 10cm) thick, about 5 to 6yds or metres apart. An overhang of 2ft (60cm) needs to be welded to the top of the metal posts at an angle of 45 degrees, or pieces of treated wood 3" x 1.5" (8 x 4cm) nailed to the top of the wooden posts. If you are using metal posts they must be drilled in 3 or 4 places, one at the end of the overhang, one above the weld where the overhang joins the post, one at ground level and an optional one where the wire nettings meet. Plain wire will be threaded through these holes and tensioned before wire netting is hung from it. In the case of wooden posts, the plain wire is threaded through wire staples which have been hammered in but not banged

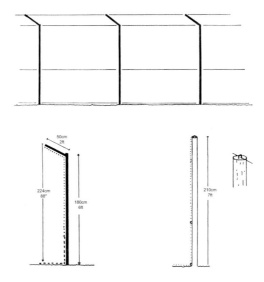

Non-electric anti-fox fencing for poultry and waterfowl.

111

home. Knock the posts in with a sledge hammer, hitting the top of the uprights, and leave 6ft (180cm) above the ground. In stony or difficult terrain the posts can be made a little shorter and a small plate welded on the bottom before they are concreted in. The wire netting at the top should be 2" (5cm) chicken wire, 6ft (180cm) wide. Clip this all the way along the plain wire at the top of the overhang, using a clipping gun and pulling it as tight as possible as you go. Then push the netting back to the posts and clip it onto the next plain wire, the one at the top of the uprights. You will have to cut and fold the netting round corners. A stronger wire netting will be needed for the bottom part of the fence; the minimum requirement is 1" (2.5cm) by 5ft (150cm) but this is not badger proof so you may need to go for badger wire (Tornado Wire Products, Bidford-on-Avon, Warwickshire), chain link or weldmesh. The badger wire is 39" (1m) small mesh sheep wire, and can be joined to the 2" (5cm) chicken wire with clips. If you decide to do this you will need wire netting 7ft (210cm) wide along the top.

The bottom or ground wire netting can be laid on the turf and secured with pegs. This will allow the grass to grow up over it and hold it down. If the ground is stony or difficult, (chalk, shale, flints etc.) it is best to bury the bottom of the wire netting. Dig a trench 2 to 3ft (60 to 90cm) wide and 6 to 9" (15 to 23cm) deep along the outside edge of the posts. Take the wire netting down to the bottom and lay it along the floor then cover it with soil and back fill. You can use either a small mechanical digger or a single furrow plough to dig this trench.

Clip the two horizontal bands of netting together and fasten them both to the plain wire if you have put one at this position. Then clip the bottom netting to the ground level strand of wire and fold the netting onto the grass or into the trench. Peg down or back fill. The corner posts will need stays or leaners on the inside so that the plain wire can be tensioned with bottle screws or radisseurs.

B)   The second method of enclosure is similar to the first without the overhang, and incorporates a net over the top. This has the advantage of keeping out winged predators like crows and magpies, but must be monitored

112

when there are heavy falls of snow as the weight could cause the fencing to collapse. The perimeter fence can be higher if required, up to 8 to 10ft (240 to 300cm), and you will need support poles and lengths of plain wire running across the inside area to hold up the 1.5" (4cm) netting across the top.

Access to the enclosure is important both for people and sometimes machinery. A timber frame 6ft (180cm) high and 8 to 10ft (240 to 300cm) wide must be constructed and don't forget to incorporate a small gate for your own use. This frame should sit on a railway sleeper or concrete plinth to deter foxes from digging underneath, and can be wired or screwed to the fence posts either side. Just remove the frame when you need access for machinery.

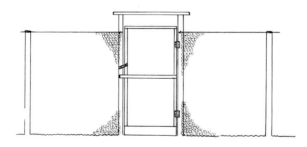

A simple 3' (90 cm) gate for access to the poultry run. The cross bar over the gate keeps the posts at equi-distance and allows for the fence top plain wire to be tensioned without the need for leaners.

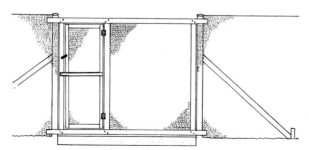

This is a double access gate for people and vehicles normally 8' wide and the whole frame can be lifted away from the two posts. The frame sits on an 8' sleeper to prevent foxes from digging in and is normally wired or bolted to the posts.

Anti-fox poultry fence.

Close up of anti-fox fence showing badger proof wire.

Pheasant release pen without electric fencing using 1" wire mesh dug into the gound and Gamenet.

Internal dividing fences for poultry. Not fox proof.

Electric Fencing

Although you can use single strands of wire for poultry, most people use the purpose made netting. In this case you are not only keeping the hens in but also keeping the fox out. This type of fencing works well for free range layers and meat birds but should never be used with goslings. The posts, normally 14, come as an integral part of the netting which is 50m long.

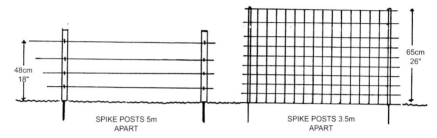

Electric fencing for free range poultry.

The second design of fencing is cheaper, involving 6ft (180cm) 1" or 2" (2.5cm or 5cm) chicken wire and incorporating electric wire. Although this

A combination of non-electric and low electric fencing to maintain an open view.

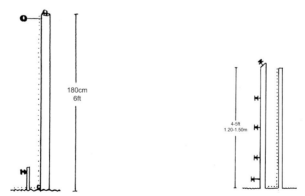

Two methods of electric fencing.

115

system works well it does have its drawbacks. First, the batteries or mains electric supply for working the energiser must be reliable; second, the top wire could be earthed by a twig or branch and will need to be checked regularly, and third, the grass under the electric wire must be kept short to prevent earthing. The fence posts are normally 8ft (240cm) long, 3 to 4" (8 to 10cm) thick, knocked in the ground 2ft (60cm) and about 4 to 5yds or metres apart. There are usually two plain tensioned wires, one at the top and one at ground level, and the 2" (5cm) chicken wire is clipped onto these, top and bottom and pegged to the ground. The electric fencing consists of two wires, one above the other 6 to 7" (15 to 18cm) apart and the bottom one 6 to 7" above the ground. These are held in place by plastic insulators nailed to 2" x 2" (5 x 5cm) stakes about 8 to 10yds or metres apart. You can buy special plastic fencing posts for this job. There is a third electric wire running along the top of the fence. It is held in place by insulators attached to pieces of 2" x 1"(5 x 2.5cm) wood 9" (23cm) long, nailed to the tops of the fence posts at 90 degrees and facing outwards. This is to stop any jumping foxes. It is important to keep clear an area of about 1yd or metre inside the fence to prevent ducks or geese from nesting too close to the perimeter, as this will encourage foxes.

Hens behind electric netting

116

Chapter 15   Tree Guards

Tree guards come in a variety of shapes and sizes. It is very important to protect trees from damage caused by livestock or hares and rabbits, who will chew leaves and branches, rub against them or de-bark them. Here are some examples of tree guards.

A square 'guard' approximately 10ft x 10ft (3m x 3m) made of four posts, rails and livestock wire has much to recommend it in large open spaces such as parks. It allows the tree to grow without any challenge from other trees and without the risk of damage from animals or farm machinery. It also provides protection for an important conservation area round the tree, although the trunk will need a spiral guard to prevent damage from rabbits. Don't forget to spray periodically round the base of the tree to keep it clear of vegetation and benefit its growth.

Triangular tree guards are better for people who need to use as much agricultural land between their trees as possible. These guards work well and come in various designs.

Metal tree guards are very elegant but are more expensive. They set young trees off well but have to be removed as the trees mature.

A cheap tree guard to protect against sheep and rabbits is made from a plastic deer guard tube wired top and bottom to a stake either side to hold it in place; it works very well against our Jacob sheep!

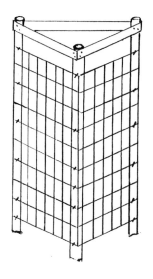

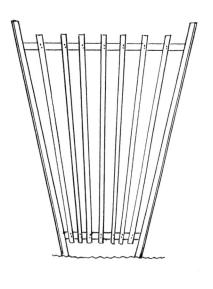

Different types of tree guard.

Different types of tree guard.

119

Chapter 16   Stiles

Stiles and their designs are covered in our book "Gates and Stiles" in the Gold Cockerel Series. There are four basic types, those you climb over, those you walk through, combinations of both and mechanical stiles.

To many people walking in the country a stile can be an obstacle, and I think a lot of the approved stiles are certainly difficult to use, which must be why a number of authorities are now using gates instead. I can't help feeling this is a pity as stiles are interesting and individual things as well as being part of our heritage.

A lot of walkers these days are not in their first flush of youth. Added to this, they often carry rucksacks and could easily become unsteady while clambering over an awkward obstacle. But stiles don't have to be difficult to negotiate. Here are two designs which I use regularly. They are simple to make and are stock proof as well as being easy to climb over.

The Beater's stile

This is not really suitable for a Public Right of Way but serves as an easy method of getting over a modern fence.

Beater's stile.

The Three Steps stile

This is one of the easiest stiles to negotiate thanks to the all important pole which is also incorporated into the Beater's stile. Anyone getting over can hold onto the pole to steady themselves, with no risk of wobbling or slipping. Unfortunately there is no pole on any of the so called 'approved' stiles today.

Three Steps stile.

Chapter 17   General Maintenance

To maintain your fences you must walk along them and check them regularly for 'rockers', that is any stakes or posts that have broken or rotted through. If you find one, remove the staples and take out the post, then make a pilot hole next to the old one with a crowbar. Bang in a new post and staple the wire back. You may also find the odd staple pulled out here and there, so replace those as well.

If you carry out checks like this once every year during the winter you should ensure your fences stay in good condition for decades to come.

Chapter 18　Fencing Standards

I have not attempted to deal with the numerous fencing standards that have been created by over zealous agencies during the last few years. How you fence your land should be dictated by the kind of stock that needs to be kept in or out, the type of land or terrain you are working on, local knowledge, and your finances. Fencing is also an evolving process with new ideas and products being developed all the time. I well remember fencing in Australia many years ago and using the same techniques back in England to the consternation of the local MAFF official, as he was then; he was seriously concerned because the techniques were not in accordance with those laid down by the rules and regulations of the day.

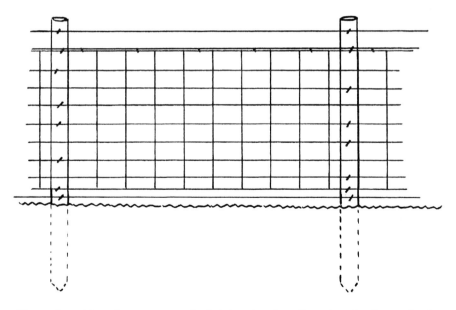

Two points: Note the extra strand of plain wire ring clipped to the livestock wire to give extra strength. Secondly, the line of plain wire along the bottom.

Chapter 19   Fencing Tips

Here are a few tips that you should find useful when fencing.

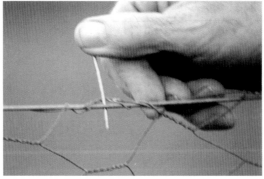

Wire twisting

Wire twisting

If you haven't any rings or ring pliers for joining wire netting to plain wire there is another easy way to do it. Take a short 2" (5cm) length of high tensile plain wire or a nail without its head, and use it to hook the top of the wire netting up and over the strand of plain wire above it; then turn the length of high tensile wire (or the nail) end over end to wind the top of the wire netting round the plain wire (see illustration). This should make a reasonably secure join.

Staples

Always hammer in staples diagonally across the grain of the timber and not in line with it to prevent the stake from splitting and to stop the staple from working loose when the stake dries out.

If you look at a staple you will notice that one side is slightly longer than the other. This means that you can push the longer end into the wood to position it easily and accurately, and also slant it at any angle you require. You will find it easier to hammer in a staple if the longer point is on the lower side.

Strimming

If you need to keep a livestock wire fence tidy, fix a strand of plain wire along the bottom. This will allow you to strim under the livestock wire without damaging it.

Tidying up

Having completed a section of fencing it's important to clear up all the odd bits of wire, old staples and off-cuts of wood before you move on. It would be very easy to chuck them in the hedge, but don't do that, put the metal in a strong plastic bag and take the wood home to burn on your fire.

Useful Addresses

S.W. & J. Dallyn,
Joydale, Kemacott,
Parracombe,
N. Devon,
EX31 4QP.
Tel: 01598 763276

Gallagher Power Fence (UK) Ltd.,
Curriers Close,
Canley,
Coventry,
CV4 8AW.
Tel: 0870 2010101

Gamekeepa Feeds Ltd, (Gamenet)
Southerly Park,
Binton,
Stratford-on-Avon
CV37 9TU.
Tel: 01789 772429

Browns Agricultural Machinery Co. Ltd.,
(Post Hammer)
Mentmore Road,
Leighton Buzzard,
LU7 2NX
Tel: 01525 375157

Gripple Ltd.,
The Old West Gun Works,
Savile Street East,
Sheffield,
S4 7UQ.
Tel: 0114 2752255

Meade Machines Ltd.,
Tisbury,
Wiltshire.
Tel: 01747 873150
(suppliers of Post Punchers)

Tornado Wire Ltd.,
Waterloo Road Estate,
Bidford-on-Avon,
B50 4JH
Tel: 0870 7593610